A Kist O' Whistles

A Kist O' Whistles

SCOTTISH FOLK TALES
Retold

by

Moira Miller

Illustrated by MAIRI HEDDERWICK

ANDRE DEUTSCH

First published in 1990 by
André Deutsch Limited
105-106 Great Russell Street, London WC1B 3LJ

Text copyright © 1990 by Moira Miller
Illustrations copyright © 1990 by Mairi Hedderwick
All rights reserved

ISBN 0 233 98538 7 (hardback)
ISBN 0 233 98537 9 (paperback)

Printed in Great Britain by
WBC Bristol and Maesteg

A Kist is the old Scottish
name for a large wooden chest

A Kist O' Whistles
was the name given to
an organ

I like to think of the Kist O' Whistles
as an old barrel organ, playing the same
much-loved tunes, over and over – bringing
back happy memories to those who already
know them, and delighting those to whom
they are completely new.

Contents

Nae Guid'll Come O' It

There was a landlord who came with his pretty daughter, Euphemia, from Edinburgh, to buy a country inn.

"Aye, Phemie, I can see us making a rare fortune in this place." He rubbed his hands in glee. He was a canny businessman and he knew that the inn was already popular.

But that was not quite good enough for him, and as soon as he moved in changes had to be made. He rebuilt bedrooms, bought new furniture, fresh curtains and carpets and repainted everything, inside and out.

"Man, ye're making a right clamjamfray o' this place," grumbled the oldest local into his beer. "Nae guid'll come o' it, I tell ye!"

But nobody listened to him.

Word got round, as word will, and soon the inn became the place to stop on the road to Edinburgh. Should the day be hot, dry and dusty the weary traveller could always be certain of a cold drink and a seat under the shady trees that grew around the courtyard. On a winter night the golden light from the windows shone out across the snow, welcoming many a poor frozen soul in to the comfort of a warm fireside and a fine meal cooked by the landlord's pretty daughter.

"There's no finer cook in the Kingdom o' Scotland than

my Phemie," he boasted, hoping to find her a husband from among the richer customers.

"Och, faither, ye're havering!" laughed Phemie, who had a great deal more sense than he did. "If you've time to talk nonsense, you've time to gie me a hand folding these sheets."

They said that the most comfortable night's sleep anywhere was to be had in the big fourposter bed in the upstairs front room. After one of Phemie's magnificent meals the crisp white lavender scented sheets welcomed the weary traveller, and in the morning the sun seemed all the brighter for shining through the tiny diamond-patterned window that looked out over the courtyard.

The landlord prospered and became rich. Able enough, at any rate, to provide a good marriage tocher for his daughter. Although there was no thought of marriage in Phemie's head, she charmed all the young men who passed through, without ever setting her heart on any one of them.

"If I'm to be wed," she said. "He'll need to have a great deal more to offer than fine words and a taste for good food and drink! And I haven't met a lad yet that I fancy."

And so things might have gone on – and our story might have ended there, had it not been for one thing.

The Wee Folk.

It's a well known fact amongst the older country people that you don't meddle with the Wee Folk, there's no telling the consequences.

"Ye maun keep that old horse-shoe nailed to the door," they warned the landlord. "Cold iron will keep their mischief out." But the landlord was from Edinburgh and knew a thing or two himself. Besides he was not for banging holes in his new paintwork.

"Nae guid'll come o' it, I'm telling ye," said the oldest local into his beer. But the landlord just laughed.

Two weeks later he had some landscape gardeners in and they cut down the big rowan tree by the door. It was blocking the light into the new sun lounge.

Word went round the village in no time.

"Cut doon the rowan tree! Man that's asking for trouble. It was the wan thing that stood between him and the Wee Folk."

"Nae guid'll come o' it," said the oldest local, and he took to drinking in a different pub. But that didn't bother the landlord, he still had plenty of other customers.

Until one night, when an important businessman stopped at the inn. He very much enjoyed his meal, and particularly asked to sleep in the fourposter in the front bedroom.

"Aye. I think you've made a real hit there, lass," said the landlord hugging his daughter as they watched the businessman climb the stairs to bed.

"Ach, faither," said Phemie, poking him in the ribs, but you could see she was quite pleased all the same.

In the morning, however, the business man came downstairs looking grey and tired.

"What ails you, sir?" asked Phemie. "Are you no' weel?"

"I was before I came here," he moaned. "But such a night as that I hope never to spend again! It was fine and comfortable until I shut my eyes, and then I was pulled and twisted, teased and pushed. Never a wink of sleep did I get from sunset to sunrise."

He was in such a state he had time only to snatch a quick cup of tea, and left without paying the bill.

The landlord and his daughter were horrified. They rushed upstairs, threw open the little window, stripped the sheets and mattress from the bed, but there was no sign of anything that might have caused the trouble.

"I doubt but he's a gey restless sleeper," laughed the landlord, uneasily.

Two nights later another traveller slept in the room, and the same thing happened again. He was so twisted and tormented that he did not even wait for daybreak. Down the stairs he clattered, and off into the darkness as if the hounds of Hell were after him.

The landlord was mystified. But the oldest local knew what was what.

"You can be sure it's the Wee Folk," he said. "I tell't him nae guid would come o' it . . ."

Word got round, as word will, and in time travellers began to pass by the inn, fearing even to stop for food or drink. The landlord became thinner, his purse grew smaller, and Phemie, seeing her chances of a husband disappearing, began to look very unhappy. Something had to be done.

The landlord himself spent a night in the room.

He climbed into his nightshirt, switched out the light, and lay in the darkness – waiting and watching for hour after hour. But nothing happened. All was quiet.

"Aye, man," he stretched and yawned. "I doubt it's all a great deal of nonsense about nothing." He plumped up the pillow, turned over on his side, closed his eyes, and drifted off to sleep.

"Aaaaaaaooooowwwww!" His yell woke everyone in the inn. "Help! Yeeeeeeeouch! Gerroff!"

Something pinched and pulled and poked him all over.

"Gerroff! Gerroff!" he shouted, hitting out at a little dark shape that flitted round the bed, up the posts, swinging from the curtains, leaving an evil smell wherever it went.

"Hee hee hee!" it chuckled wickedly, easily avoiding the landlord blundering in the darkness.

"Faither, are you all right!" Phemie banged on the door. "Whit is it?" She burst in, and switched on the light just in time to see something small and dark whirl into the fireplace and up the chimney.

"What in the name of all conscience was that?" she gasped. The landlord shook his head, too shocked to speak.

The next morning he put a notice in the local paper to the effect that any man who could rid the inn of the wicked little creature could have a half-share in the place and marry Phemie.

Word spread, as word will, and a couple of Sunday papers noticed the story and did full-page articles. The oldest local was interviewed, and even put his false teeth in for the photograph. He gave it as his opinion that the inn had been taken over by a Brownie.

"And they're gey difficult to shift wance they get a fit in the door," he said. "You mark my words, if there's wan in

5

the hoose, there'll be mair ootside waiting to join him."

In no time at all the inn was full again, this time with young men full of ideas for clearing out the Brownie.

"I'm not sure this was a good idea, faither," said Phemie, looking at the strange looking collection who sat in the bar every night. The oldest local sat in a corner, quietly enjoying it all. One by one the young men tried. There were some who rang bells all night, others who burned strange smelling candles, yet others who walked up and down chanting spells,

but the Brownie just laughed. He blew out their candles, made fun of their spells, and kicked the bells around the room until nobody in the village could sleep, never mind the inn.

At last, one spring morning, there came a tall dark-haired young man. He was just passing through, on the way from Glasgow, and had not heard about the Brownie. He had a quiet drink, and chatted to the oldest local, then he stayed on for a bar lunch and another glass of something, and winked at Phemie. For the first time in weeks she smiled back. In no time at all the landlord told him the story of his troubles, and the Brownie in the bedroom.

"You want him out?" laughed the dark-haired lad. "Then I'm your man, I'll soon see him off the premises." Phemie was so delighted she cooked him a magnificent meal and that night, at bedtime, with a small nightlight candle, a bottle of the landlord's best wine and two glasses, she led him upstairs to the front bedroom.

He pulled a chair over to the fireside, lit the tiny candle, stretched out and poured himself a glass or two of wine. He yawned and closed his eyes, pretending to fall asleep.

Presently there was a tweak at the toe of his boot. He opened one eye. In front of him stood an evil-smelling little creature like a badly tied heap of brown sacking. Its eyes were black and gleaming in a face like an old wrinkled apple.

"Och, it's jist you," said the young man, yawning. "How dare ye disturb a great man like Myself!" The Brownie rolled about laughing.

"I thocht ye were asleep," he hooted. "Yir a bit different to the usual lot. Who are ye onyway?"

"I told ye, wee man – Myself. That's who I am." The young man stretched and sat up reaching for the bottle. "Might as well have a wee nip. Will ye join me?"

"Don't mind if I do," said the Brownie. "Here, go easy, Mr. Myself, that's rather a lot yir pouring there."

The Brownie knocked back the wine and as soon as his glass was empty, it was refilled. He stretched out on the rug with a smelly belch and began telling outrageous stories. The young man refilled his own glass, pretending to become drunk, but he poured the wine into a vase of flowers. At last he dropped his glass and stretched out snoring in the chair.

"Hee hee hee! At last!" The Brownie chuckled wickedly,

pulled a sharp stick from the pile of wood by the fire, and crept over to the chair.

"Right, wee man, I'm ready for you!" shouted the dark haired lad and quick as a flash he seized the Brownie in one hand, the stick in the other, and beat the wicked little creature till he screamed and howled for mercy.

"Yeeeeeeouch! Eeeeeeeahhh!" he screeched. His cries floated up the chimney to his friends who had come to sit on the roof and enjoy the fun.

"Whit's happening doon there?" shouted the Wee Folk. "Whit are ye daen? Wha's hurting ye?"

"It's Myself?" shrieked the Brownie who by this time was black and blue all over. "It's Myself that's hurting me! Ohhh, yeeeeeouch! Oh, Mammy Daddy! Help!"

"He's hurting himself?" said the Wee Folk on the roof, and they scratched their heads, fair amazed that anyone could be so stupid.

"Say that again!" they shouted.

"It's Myself. Owwwwwww!" howled the wicked wee Brownie as the young man skelped him round the room. "It's Myself that's hurtin' me! Stop it! Stop it!"

The more he shouted, the more the Wee Folk laughed, until at last, quite helpless, they rolled off the roof and fell in an untidy heap in the courtyard where Phemie was ready. She took a big stiff brush, bundled them all out into the road, and locked the gate behind them.

"Away and don't bother us again!" she shouted after them, and they were so ashamed when they realised how they had been tricked that they never did. One thing the Wee Folk cannot take is being made to look stupid.

The dark haired lad from Glasgow married Phemie of course, and they're living happily ever after. The only wee folk creating mischief at the inn now are the landlord's grandchildren, and the place is always busy, full of laughter, good food and wine. Besides which it's on the Fairies and Phantoms Tourist Board Route marked 'not to be missed'.

"A' these coach trips," muttered the oldest local into his beer. "Nae guid'll come o' it . . ." But nobody listens to him.

And if you go there with one of the tours, you'll have a comfortable night, even in the upstairs front bedroom with the four poster, because Phemie planted a wee rowan tree in the courtyard the morning after the Brownies left. And, just to be sure, there's an iron horse shoe nailed up on the new paint of the front door.

The Stealing of Christie McHarg

Sandy McHarg hauled on his right oar, pulling the heavy wooden skiff side on to the long slow swell of the high tide. He slid his arms out of his leather jerkin, and paused for breath.

It was his favourite time of day, the summer dim before nightfall with the western sky a flaring red gold, and the air warm and breathless. Across the glassy water he could catch quite clearly the voices from his own farmyard. That must be Christie telling the herdboy to make sure the barn was locked and the beasts were safe.

He smiled at the thought of Christie. It hardly seemed possible even now, six months after the event, that she had agreed to marry him. She could have had her pick of the young men from Dumfries to Castle Douglas, aye, and far beyond, but there she was, the belle of every dance in the county with her chestnut curls and sparkling eyes, sitting at his own hearth side, Mistress Alexander McHarg. For the thousandth time he blessed his good luck.

Time he was home.

He peered carefully into the gathering darkness taking his line of sight from the broken mast of the ship that had lain wrecked on the headland these last three winters. Along the

beach, past the rocks, he could just see his own farm steading, square and grey against the soft blue green of the Galloway hills behind. Very soon now Christie would set a lamp in the window, he would draw in his net for the last time, catch the current and pull for shore.

But with very little to show for this evening's fishing. Either the air was too heavy or the fish hung, sleepy, in the shifting currents of the Solway Firth, but the big wicker creel lay empty at his feet.

There was only one place he had not tried. One place he knew there would be fish worth catching. But still — Sandy McHarg shivered slightly, then he laughed and shook his head.

"Old wives' tales and superstitions," he muttered, and hauled on the oars, heading for the shattered mast. There were always fish to be caught around the wreck during the day, they swam in and out of the rotting cabins, feeding on the rich sea weed. But in the dark? Well that was very different. Nobody went near the ship after sunset.

With the passing years, the stories had grown wilder. The wreck was said to be haunted by water elves, or sea fairies or whatever. Old man Laurie, from over Balcreggan way, had staggered into the McHarg's kitchen one night, white as a shroud, with some tale of having seen lights on the ship, and heard weird, unearthly laughter.

"I would say he'd taken just a wee bit much to drink," said Christie watching him leave at last. "But he's no' just that sort of man."

"Aye, Mistress Laurie makes sure o' that!" laughed Sandy, and they shrugged off the stories.

But out there, alone, in the wee boat in the half-dark, with the eerie cry of an oyster catcher echoing across the silken water, Sandy was not just so sure. He took a deep breath, and whistling a reel to himself, set a rhythm for the oars.

Under the dark shape of the ruined hull the wee waves slapped and chuckled with a sound that was almost human. The water here was restless, constantly shifting, and what little wind there was whispered in the ropes left hanging from the broken yardarm. Sandy shipped his oars and cast his net into the blackness, watching the weed fingers reach out to stroke it. He was right though, there were fish down there. There was a quick glint of silver and three gleaming mackerel came up in the first throw. Encouraged, he went on, forgetting his fears, and the creeping darkness.

He was gathering the net for the fourth time when he heard the sound.

Tunc-tunc-tunc-tunc. It was a soft, rhythmic beat from deep in the hull. His throat choked. He froze, listening.

Tunc-tunc-tunc-tunc. A pause. And then it came again, vibrating through the thin shell of the skiff. Slow and steady as a heartbeat, felt rather than heard, it was the sound of a hatchet cutting into wood, somewhere far beneath the boat.

Sandy felt the hair prickle on the back of his neck and became aware suddenly that the last of the light had faded from the sky and the sea. The water was a dead, cold grey and the old hulk a mass of shifting shadows. He could feel his heart thumping. The sound echoed again.

Tunc-tunc-tunc-tunc. He laughed suddenly, a quick gasp of relief.

"It'll be the tide turning. Like as not it's catching some loose piece of wood. I'd best get home."

He pulled on the net, desperate now to get back to the shore, it jerked in his hands, catching on something beneath the boat. He leaned over the gunwale to free the mesh and saw, far beneath him in the green water a light shining in the shattered hull.

"The Lord preserve us!" he whispered hoarsely. The net ran through his hands and sank, as a weird unearthly laugh rang out.

Tunc-tunc-tunc-tunc. The pace quickened. A pause, and then the blood chilled in his veins as a shrill cry echoed back.

"Ho there, brither, whit is it that ye're daein' noo sae thrang wi' yir hammer and chisel?"

The steady beat stopped. There was silence for the lift of a wave and then came another voice, slow and terrible from the deeps of the sea.

"I'm making a wife for Sandy McHarg! I mean to leave her for him, an' tak his ain for masel'." Wild laughter echoed like the howl of wind in the rigging.

"Dear God, no!" Sandy grabbed the oars, as the voice rang around his head, cruel as the cry of a cormorant.

"A wife for Sandy McHarg!"

Like a man possessed he rowed for the shore. Half-mad with fear, he left the fish in the boat and raced up the path from the beach. The light still shone from the window, warm and safe. He fell in the door and slammed it behind him, retching for breath.

"The shutters woman! Bar the windows, quickly!"

"Sandy! Whatever's the matter?"

"Just do as I tell you!" he shouted, dragging the big heavy kitchen table over against the door. As Christie fastened the shutters, he reached down the family Bible and laid it open on the table. That entrance at least was barred, he turned to the rest of the room.

"The chimney. The chimney's open . . . Christie, we have to stop them!" He seized a handful of salt and threw it on the flames of the open hearth.

"Alexander McHarg, have you taken leave . . .?"

"Wheesht!" he said, grasping hold of her arm. As the old wag-at-the-wa' clock struck midnight, the farmyard echoed to the clatter of a horse's hooves, and a fist hammered on the door.

"Mistress McHarg! Mistress McHarg! Ye maun come noo, yir help is needed. Old Mistress Laurie is sick and cries for ye!"

Christie struggled to free herself.

"Let me go, Sandy. The woman's ailing. She needs me. Let me go!" But Sandy held tight.

"Supposing all the laird's wives in Galloway were calling for you this night. You must not set foot outside this house!" He roared the words for all to hear. In the yard, the horse wheeled and whinnied, and a shouted oath rang back, as the hoofbeats faded into the night.

Sandy relaxed his hold on his wife. She stared at him, shaking her head in wonder.

"Sandy. Whatever is it? What has happened to you?"

"Pray, woman, pray for the both of us!" He fell to his knees, dragging her with him. "May the dear Lord protect us from witches, ghosts, goblins and a' the fiends o' Hell,

should they be led by auld Nick himself . . ."

"Sandy! The barn! The barn's on fire!" Through the cracks in the shutters came a glare, as if a fireball had struck the yard. Smoke seeped beneath the door and filled the kitchen, black and choking. Above the crackling of burning wood they heard the terrified lowing of the cows, and the dogs barking, frantic with fear.

"NO!" Sandy grabbed his wife as she reached to open the shutters. "No, Christie. Stay with me! I beg you, do as I say. Trust me." He pulled her close to him, covering her ears as the bellowing from the yard grew louder and the flames crackled higher, and above all a high shrill laugh rang out.

For hours they crouched in the corner and listened as the fire raged round the farmstead. Whiles it seemed to die away, and other times it seemed as if the tongues of flame licked at their very door, charring the wood. But still Sandy held tight to his wife and together they knelt in the kitchen praying silently.

At last, with the first fingers of dawn across the sky, there came a final ear-splitting scream, the laughter died away and the farmyard fell silent.

A burnt log slumped into ash in the dying fire and the old clock measured a slow quiet tick as Sandy and Christie gazed at each other, red-eyed and exhausted.

"Is it over?" Her throat was dry, her voice hoarse from the smoke. Out in the apple tree, an early blackbird welcomed the sun.

"Aye. It's over . . . we've beaten them I'm thinking."

Slowly, stiffly, Sandy helped her to her feet and together they opened the door.

The sun glowed through the summer mist across the silver firth. Alone and stark in the soft morning air, the masts of the old wreck pierced the shining water. A lone gull, hunting for food, hung lazy against the blue sky. The world was new, fresh and sea clean, but with a faint tang still of sulphur.

The farmyard was scrubbed and neat as always. In the barn the cows lowed softly, waiting to be milked. Jess the sheepdog lay sleeping in the straw, and the herdboy came whistling up the lane.

Sandy shook his head in disbelief. Had the night ever happened at all then? Had it all been some terrible dream?

"Look!" Christie pointed, her voice shaking with fear. "Whit devil's trickery was here, d'ye think?"

Discarded in a corner of the yard, blackened and burned, was an ancient, rotting piece of ship's timber. It had been violently shattered, as though destroyed in frustrated fury, but it was still possible to see that some cunning hand had chopped and chiselled the wood, until it had taken on the form of a woman – and of a woman about the same size and shape as Mistress Christie McHarg.

Jamie And The Puddocks

There was once a King who had three sons. The older two, Angus and Donald, were twins. They were pleasant enough big lads, noisy and full of fun. But as the King's Chief Adviser had been heard to say, privately of course, 'two half wits do not make a whole one.' They were fond of practical jokes, and were forever teasing their younger brother Jamie. He took after his mother, small, fair, a bit dreamy sometimes, but very much brighter than the other two. And that would not have been difficult.

Now it happened, as it does, that with the passing years the old King became unwell. A wee twinge of indigestion here, a creak of arthritis there. He went to one or two funerals of folk he had been at school with, and began to think perhaps he really ought to decide which of his sons should succeed him as King. It was difficult because naturally the twins were exactly the same age, and they argued endlessly and noisily about who should inherit the crown.

"Whatever am I to do?" sighed the King.

"Convene a Committee of all the Wise Men in the Kingdom, Your Majesty," said his Chief Adviser, "and ask them." He was a great one for passing the buck.

"Aye, right enough," said the King, "that's what Wise Men are for. They might as well work for their money."

The Wise Men came from everywhere. It was hard to believe there were so many in the Kingdom. The Committee formed several sub-committees who dithered and deliberated and by the end of a year and a day they had run up a massive bill for paper and coffee, produced hundreds of reports, and the King was no wiser.

"Whatever am I to do?" he sighed. His wife, the Queen, who was a sensible woman, put down her book, smiled and shook her head.

"It seems to me, dearest, that a wee bit of common-sense is needed here," she said. "Look at it this way, whoever becomes King will have to be responsible for taking care of a great deal of gold, and particularly the crown jewels. Right?"

"True enough," said the King.

"Then why not be sure that they know their worth?" said the Queen. "Set the boys a task. Like – em – send them off to find the most beautiful ring in the world. And give them a time limit. A year and a day sounds about right."

"It does indeed," said the King, imagining the peace and quiet of a year and a day without Angus and Donald. He went off to tell the Wise Men that he himself had thought of an answer to their problem.

The appointed time came for the princes to leave, but there was an argument about that too.

"I shall go north," said Angus, saddling up his horse.

"No, I was going to do that," roared Donald, "You can go south." Jamie shook his head, laughed and sat on the steps crunching an apple.

"The three of you will go where I tell you," snapped the Queen.

"The THREE of us?" said Angus, Donald and Jamie with one voice.

"You heard," said the Queen. "Now come with me." She led them up a twisting spiral stair to the top of the highest tower in the castle, and then handed each of them a white feather.

"Drop that over the edge," she said, "And whatever way the wind takes it, that's the way you will go."

Angus took his feather and dropped it. It floated down, then lifting on the wind, whirled off towards the distant blue line of the northern mountains.

"Ha ha!" he roared. "There is fine gold to be had in the mountains. My ring will have the rarest setting."

"Soon see about that," said Donald and he threw his feather high in the air. It was caught and whisked high into the sunlight towards the soft green lands of the south.

"And MY ring," he said, "will have the rarest diamonds."

They turned on Jamie, who shrugged, took his feather and dropped it over the edge. The wind died and the little feather drifted, twisting and turning to the cobble stones of the palace courtyard far beneath them. Angus and Donald roared with laughter.

"Poor wee Jamie," gasped Angus. "I doubt but you'll have to spend the year searching among the pots and pans in the kitchen for your ring!" Their laughter still echoed round the castle long after they had ridden out to fulfill their tasks.

Poor Jamie indeed. What chance did he have of finding a fine ring in the puddles outside his own kitchen door. For months he moped about the castle, reading the postcards his brothers sent back, and not even taking the trouble to hunt for his feather.

"There's but a month left of your year, Jamie," said his mother. "Time you were out there searching I'm thinking."

"Aye, all right," he sighed, and went off out to the courtyard, most unwillingly.

The feather lay almost hidden in a dank corner, overgrown with moss and ferns. He would have missed it, but that it stood up straight and white against the green. As Jamie went to pick it up, he tripped and stubbed his toe against a heavy iron ring set in the stone.

"Whatever's this?" he wondered, and remembering a story he had read somewhere about buried gold, lifted the ring and heaved on it. Slowly, slowly the flagstone came up like a trapdoor and a gust of foul, damp smelling air hit him. He coughed, and stepped back, dropping the stone. But not before he had seen the steps vanishing down into the darkness of a tunnel beneath the castle. Jamie had that stone up again in a flash.

The steps were old and worn and twisted down and round into the darkness of an earth floored tunnel. Behind him the glow of daylight faded to a pinprick and very soon Jamie found himself in intense darkness and silence. It was as if a black quilt had fallen around him.

His footsteps faltered. He reached out and his fingertips on either side touched cold slimy stone. He swallowed hard and stepped back.

"Mind whaur yir pittin' yir great boots," grunted a voice behind him.

"Aaaagh!" Jamie let out a yell and whirled round. At his feet was a faint green glow. As he struggled to catch his breath, the glow brightened and he could see that it came from a large green frog squatting at his feet.

"A puddock?" he whispered hoarsely.

"Aye. A puddock, whit else were ye expecting?" The creature's hooded black eyes watched him closely. Jamie shook his head.

"Man, ye've been a lang time comin'," grumbled the frog. "Ye've no' left us much time tae find yir ring. Noo follow me, and dinna waste ony mair time." It hopped over Jamie's feet and bounced off, the green light fading away down the tunnel.

"Here, wait for me!" shouted Jamie stumbling along behind. Up and down he climbed, over rocks and stones, through an underground stream and then suddenly round a corner he tumbled down a gravel slope and sat up – astonished.

"Close yir mooth," said the frog rudely. "Ye'll catch flies like that." Jamie clambered to his feet and stared around him.

The tunnel opened out into a vast vaulted hall. The walls seemed to be of soft green moss, flecked with gold, and the floor stretching in front of him was a sheet of shining crystal. In the centre of the floor stood a large low stone table, laden

with plates and cups of gold, and around it, drinking, eating and singing rowdily, were other frogs.

"Hundreds of them," whispered Jamie in amazement.

"Aye, weel, dozens onywey," said his guide. "Come away in and join us in a glass of wine." Still dazed, Jamie allowed himself to be dragged across to the table. A golden goblet of wine was pressed into his hand and in an enchanted haze of music and laughter, he soon forgot his life in the castle above their heads.

But the frog had not forgotten. At the end of a month he took Jamie by the hand and led him from the table, back into the dark tunnel.

"Time ye were away hame noo," he said. "Yir brithers are back wi' their bonny rings. High time ye gied them yours." He pressed something into the young man's hand and led him slipping and stumbling, back up to the worn steps, leaving him blinking in the daylight of the courtyard.

The ring was exquisite. Cunningly made of twisting gold fronds, fine as water weeds, it was set with a glowing green emerald the size of a small puddock. There can surely have been no more beautiful jewel in the whole world.

The King and Queen and the Committee of Wise Men certainly thought so when they saw it. Angus and Donald had found fine rings right enough, but nothing to equal the magnificence of Jamie's.

"It's not fair," the twins protested. "He can't possibly become King. He never even left the castle!" They made such a fuss, that for the sake of peace, the King reconvened the Committee.

"There must be one more task," he said. "Something that will prove finally which son is fit to be King in my place."

The Wise Men racked their brains, Angus and Donald argued. At last the Queen came up with the answer.

"It would seem to me," she said. "That whoever becomes King will need to have a Queen alongside him. I would like to think she has some of my – ah – good looks, and common sense."

"As ever, my dear, you've hit the nail on the head," said the King. The Committee were told to agree that whoever found the most beautiful and intelligent bride should become heir to the throne.

"Same arrangement with the feathers," said the Queen. "And mind, you've a year and a day only." Later that afternoon Angus rode south in pursuit of his bride to be, Donald rode north. Jamie hung over the battlements, watching his feather sink to the cobbles with the jeering laughter of his brothers still ringing in his ears. The frogs might just have been lucky enough to find the ring in the tunnels beneath the castle, but a princess as well? No chance of that.

He let the feather lie where it fell until at last his mother came to him.

"Two weeks left, Jamie," she said. "Away you off and find that feather."

"Och, but mother . . ." She bundled him out into the court-yard and shut the door firmly behind him.

The feather was lying, stiff and white in the iron ring.

"Here we go again," sighed Jamie, and hauling up the stone, he stumbled down the steps. He was struggling along in the darkness, desperately trying to find his way forward when a voice croaked in his ear.

"It's yirself."

"It is that," he panted, stopping for a rest.

"I thocht ye were nivver coming!" grumbled the frog. He was perched, like a green nightlight, on a rough stone shelf just above Jamie's head. "Right, now yir here, follow me." He leapt off, leaving Jamie to follow as best he could.

As he tumbled into the hall a cheer rang round the company.

"Sit ye doon, laddie. Guid tae see ye back," said one frog pulling out a chair for him, while another poured him a goblet of wine. In no time, Jamie was settled in, eating and drinking his fill with the rest of them.

At the end of two weeks, his guide and companion stood up on his chair and banged a plate on the table. Around him the laughter and singing died away.

"Harrrumph," he croaked, clearing his throat. "Fellow puddocks – and Jamie lad, we come to the business we are here to arrange. We hae a weddin' tae celebrate."

"I love weddings," said Jamie to the wee frog beside him. "All that cake and dancing. Whose is it?"

"Yours, ye daft gomeril," said the frog. "Have ye forgotten? Yir brothers are back wi' their ladies. They're bonny enough, if ye like humans. But we've found a real beauty for you. Here's yir bride!" He made a low and elegant bow, and there stepped forward a small green shiny frog, with the brightest black eyes Jamie had ever seen.

"Here – just a minute!" He jumped to his feet. "I can't marry a wee puddock. They'd say I was daft – and they'd be right."

"Come on noo," said the frog. "Did I no' find yir ring for ye?"

"Well – yes I suppose you did."

"Then trust me and dae as yir tellt. Ye'll no regret it, I'll warrant ye."

Jamie agreed at last. The floor was cleared, the others gathered round, and he and the wee green frog with the bright black eyes were married.

"There noo, that's that," said his guide happily. "Away ye go up yonder tae the castle noo, Jamie. Yir brithers are waiting wi' their brides and ye maun gang and join them. Awa' wi' ye, an' yir bride will meet ye there."

Shaking his head at his own stupidity, Jamie stumbled and staggered back along the dark passageway, up the twisting stair to the courtyard. He stood, shielding his eyes for a moment, and gradually realised that someone was waiting for him at the top of the steps into the Throne Room.

Against the shimmering sunlight she was small and slim, with a halo of long silver-fair hair. Around her shoulders hung a gleaming green silk cloak, fluid as water.

"Are you – my wee puddock?" He reached up a hand, hardly daring to believe that she was real. She smiled down at him, the bright black eyes sparkling.

"I am that, Jamie. My father was a great and important man, but he and I, and all our friends were turned into puddocks by a wicked and jealous warlock. The spell could only be broken if a prince would take my hand in marriage. And ye did." She reached down and gently kissed him.

Jamie, in an enchanted dream, took his beautiful Puddock Princess by the hand and led her into the hall. There he found the King and Queen. At their side stood a portly little gentleman in a bright green coat.

"Some wine," he declared. "We must drink a toast to my daughter and her husband."

"A man after my own heart," said the King, rising to his feet to inspect his son's bride. "She's the bonniest lass I've ever seen – well next to my own good wife," he added quickly nodding in the direction of the Queen. "I think we'll just join your friends, I must say they seem to have made themselves quite at home in the wine cellars."

There was quite a party that night. Angus and Donald had found themselves brides who were bonny enough you may be sure, but neither was as beautiful as the Puddock Princess.

"Maybe just as well," said Angus, cracking open another bottle of wine.

"Aye, you can't play practical jokes if you're a King," said Donald. "It would be a dull life."

But Jamie and his Puddock Princess never thought it a dull life when in time they became King and Queen. They loved each other dearly you see. And where you have love, life always has a sparkle.

The Seal Wife

On an island in the Orkneys, there was once a young fisherman by the name of Magnus. His parents being dead, he
lived alone, away from the rest of the village, in a cottage
his grandfather had built down by the sea shore.

Magnus was a good fisherman, as his father, grandfathers
and great grandfathers had been before him. The sea had
given his family their living, and some their deaths, through
many generations.

Where a family of farmers will leave their mark in the
fields cultivated down the centuries, his people had left their
furrows ploughed by the keels of countless ships in the hard-
ness of the rocks before the cottage. It was here he drew up
his little skiff, in the self same spot where his Viking
forefathers had beached their longboats. For Magnus, the
sea was in his soul, and he was never happy far from the
sound and taste of it.

He was a tall, fine looking lad, straw fair and blue eyed.
Sociable enough when the right mood was on him, he would
happily dance and drink the night away with his friends. But
there were other times when a wild longing came on Magnus
and then he preferred to dance alone to another tune, lured
away by the slow strathspey of swell on shingle, or the swoop-

ing reel of the gulls around his masthead. In that sort of madness he would push his tiny boat out into the roughest seas, and laugh in the teeth of the gale, daring the others to follow him.

"It is high time that one settled down and found a good wife," grumbled the young women of the village, seeing their husbands unsettled. But Magnus only laughed at them.

"What me, marry? Never in a month of Sundays."

Even his closest friend Erik found there was no talking to him on the subject. They lay, lazing in the boat one still summer afternoon, with the sun blazing down and the lines melting into a sea of green glass.

"Man, Magnus, whatever are we to do about you? You can wait too long, and then you'll end up wed to some old crone who'll steal the money out of your trouser pockets and frighten the fish." Magnus laughed and shook his head.

"I'm serious." Erik sat up. "Marry my sister Annie. She is fond of you, always has been, and besides she's a good cook and would make a fine wife."

"I know that, right enough. And Annie is bonny, for sure, but . . ." Magnus leaned over the side and drew his fingers through the cold salt water. "I'm married already – to the sea. And, hand on heart, Erik, I swear I will marry no woman unless she be like the sea, wild and free and beautiful."

"But you cannot HOLD the sea," Erik snatched a handful of water. "Look, man. It will run through your fingers. With a wife like that, no man could be happy long."

Magnus laughed, and shrugged, them trimming his sail to the west, steered for the open sea. There was no telling him anything.

Now it happened one fine evening not long after that, he was walking home alone from the village. It was Midsummer Night, a special time in the islands, and everyone had come together to celebrate. Magnus stayed late, drinking and laughing, and then once midnight had turned, set off down the path to the cottage.

The full moon shone pale and ghostly in a cool sky that was half-dark, half light. Magnus stepped out along the beach, stopping from time to time to take a drink from his bottle, and still singing to himself. As he sang the wee waves splashed and danced in time to the music, which grew louder in his head with each step. By the time he had rounded the rocks and was into the bay beneath his cottage, he was dancing to a tune that seemed to fill the whole world. It was woven into the rocks and sea, and in the clouds chasing each other across the moonlit sky.

"A fine night it is!" shouted Magnus hurling his cap in the air.

"It is! It is!" echoed back the rocks. And then they rang with a wild laughter that was not his.

Magnus froze in his tracks, stunned and suddenly sober, peering into the half light.

On the wet sand between high and low tide, there were figures, dancing. Strange beings the like of which he had never seen before. They were tall and dark, shining like fresh caught fish. In and out they skipped, over the waves where they curled onto the sand. Sometimes they seemed to melt into the water and become part of it.

Magnus sank to his knees behind a rock and watched, open mouthed. The dancing feet left no trace on the wet sand, the bodies were beautiful, wild and effortless as the wind in the grass. For minutes only he watched, and then the longing to join their dance seized him. Without pausing

to think, he jumped to his feet and ran down the beach.

But Magnus was human, and clumsy, and they heard him. Quickly they turned away and pulling on sealskins that had been left lying on the rocks, they slid silently into the water. By the time Magnus reached the wet sand they had vanished.

But one sealskin still lay at his feet, black and silky.

Alone on the rocks by the point, lost in dreams, a girl danced. Supple as seaweed, she turned and twisted until suddenly seeing Magnus holding the skin, she stopped.

"I must have it!" she gasped. "I cannot go back to my own people without it. Please! I beg you."

Magnus stared at the woman. She was as tall as he, with hair silver as moonlight. In her eyes were the green-black deeps of the sea.

"No. No," he whispered, reaching out to touch her. "You must not go back. You are the one I have been waiting for all my life. You are the wife that I must marry."

She begged pitifully, but Magnus, reaching out a finger to stroke the silver hair, stood spellbound. She sobbed, long and sore, and still he would not give back the skin. All night long she sat by his side on the sand, weeping and heartbroken.

Then at last when the sun came up in a pink haze over the sea she washed her face in a rock pool, bound back her silver hair with a strand of weed, and followed him silently to the cottage. She gave a shudder as her bare feet left the sand, and she stepped onto grass for the first time. But still she must follow the man who had claimed her, and agree to become his wife.

In no time word went round the village of the strange and beautiful woman Magnus had taken to wife, and soon they came to visit. One after another his friends and their wives called and, in return, invited him to bring his wife to the village. But Magnus had no time for them, and his wife sat silent, shaking her head. She refused to leave the cottage by the shore, and gradually Magnus realised she would neither set foot on the road to the village, nor on the path to the hills.

He saw then the way to keep her always with him. Setting out early one morning he climbed to the top of the hill behind the house and hid her sealskin under a cairn of stones amongst the heather where she would not go. For long months he watched as she wandered restlessly along the beach, climbing among the rock pools, searching, searching. But gradually she seemed to settle to life in the cottage and to accept that there was no returning to her own people.

Time passed and children were born to Magnus and his wife. There were five sons, four of them tall, sturdy children, with straw fair hair and blue eyes, but the youngest, whom his mother loved the best, was small and slim with soft silvery hair and sea-dark eyes.

Magnus loved them all and doted on his wife. She in turn seemed happy to settle down with him in the cottage. She cooked and kept the place clean and shining and would have seemed like any other wife, but for her strange moods, and the songs she sang as she worked.

They enchanted Magnus. Sometimes, singing to the children, her voice was soft and gentle as the breeze on a summer night. At other times she sang strange wild songs with the high keening note of the north wind across a winter sea. It was at those times she spent hours wandering by herself along the tideline, gazing out across the water, as if enraptured by some sound that Magnus himself could not hear. He was afraid of those times, but as the years went by they became fewer and he learned to forget his fear.

Then one day when Magnus was away at the fishing with the three older boys, the two younger ones went to play on the hillside above the cottage. They were running and hiding amongst the rocks when the smallest child found the sealskin. Never had he touched anything so beautiful. He snatched it up and, followed by his brother, ran back to the cottage.

"Mother, mother. See what I have found. See the bonny fur, it is so soft and silky."

She dropped the dishes on the table, took the fur from her son and, stroking his hair, gazed long into his sea-dark eyes. Then slowly, followed by the little ones, she left the cottage. Lifting her head until her silver hair streamed in the fresh sea-wind she walked down across the sand. Away to her left

she could see Magnus and the boys heading back towards
the beach.

Quickly she turned to the two small boys and kissed them,
then quicker still, she turned away, and lifting her skirts, ran
down to the water.

Too late, Magnus hauled on the oars. He shouted from
the boat, seeing her pull the sealskin around her shoulders
and dive into the creaming surf. Briefly her head showed
above the waves, sleek and wet, and as he and the children
watched another seal came to meet her and together the two
swam out, bobbing and dancing on the waves.

They watched, staring at the water until the seals vanished.

They watched for many years, but she never came back
again. Sometimes, though, in the hour of sunset and the quiet
of an ebbing tide, as Magnus walked along the shore he
would stop and listen. From far off, beyond the sound of the
sea and the wind, there came a sweet, wild song. And only
he and his youngest son could hear it.

Pearls For The Giantess

In the old days there were giants about. There still are, of course, but fewer of them and they tend to be a great deal less trouble than they used to be. Nowadays there's none of this rampaging about the countryside tearing up trees, they leave that to the motorway builders. Neither do they go around terrifying little girls, most of whom would be more than a match for the average giant, who isn't very bright anyway.

In the old days, though, it was different. Giants rampaged and bullied all the time, rather like large sized toddlers – very large sized toddlers. If they didn't like something they stamped on it, and if they saw something they particularly fancied, well, they just took it. No questions asked.

There was one particular giant who took a fancy to Catriona.

Catriona was certainly a very fanciable young lady. Small and plump with bright crisp ginger curls and a wicked twinkle in her eye. She was engaged to be married to Calum, the hunter and fisherman, and he, sensible lad, counted himself very lucky indeed. He was a good fisherman, but a bit soft-hearted for a hunter. He was more inclined to let the birds or animals escape, and even helped them to do so sometimes.

There was one time he found a great golden eagle with a damaged claw, and spent weeks nursing it back to health.

"Daft!" said the local folk. "It'll only come back and steal the lambs in the spring." But that was Calum, a gentle big lad. Catriona loved him anyway, and he was devoted to her.

Not only was she pretty to look at, and a good cook, she could spin wool so fine people came from miles around to buy it. You can be sure they boasted about the quality of the clothes they made from Catriona's wool, and in time it came to the notice of a giant. He had never been one to bother about his clothes, but what others had, he must have too. He could not rest until he had a suit made from the finest wool. But giants do things their own way and instead of going along to Catriona's house, and putting in an order as everyone else did, he went along and removed Catriona. Lock, stock and spinning wheel.

Off he stamped to his castle, with Catriona kicking and screaming and threatening all sorts of trouble, but of course she never had a chance. He locked her up at the top of a high tower, along with her spinning wheel and a room full of rough fleece.

"No food for you until there's enough spun to make me a warm scarf to start with," he roared. And that was that, she simply had to get on with it.

Calum of course was furious and threatened all sorts of revenge, but he had no idea where to start looking. The giant had come in the dead of night, and nobody had seen what way he went, but there was no stopping the lad.

"I'm a hunter," he said. "And I can surely track them down by myself." He packed his bow and arrows, locked up his cottage and tramped off into the hills.

He tramped for days, weeks and months through country that became bleaker and colder. He left behind the green straths with the little welcoming farmhouses and roamed high on the rocky shoulder of the mountains, but there was never a sign of the giant or Catriona.

He came at last to the top of a jagged peak and saw in every direction only more rocks, ice and bleak scree slopes. Calum sighed, slumped down, exhausted in the lee of the rocks and, with the whistling of the wind in his ears, fell asleep.

Some time later, he woke with a start, the wind had dropped because something stood in front of him, blocking the sunlight.

"Whit . . .?" He leaped to his feet, still dazed. Around his head the huge golden eagle wheeled and lifted and then gradually gliding down came to rest on the rock at his back.

"I had need of you once, brother," said the eagle, "but this day you have need of me, and I will repay my debt."

"How? Tell me how?" Calum's head was spinning, as he watched the bird.

"I have seen the woman you seek," it croaked. "She lies imprisoned in a giant's tower many miles from here, high among mountains where no man has ever set foot. You have only to climb upon my back and I will take you to her."

Calum needed no second invitation. Gulping back fear, he closed his eyes and threw his arms about the bird's neck. High above the mountains they soared, deep in the clouds where ice hung about them and his hands lost all feeling. Down they swooped into dark valleys where the pine trees grew tall and close in the sour earth and sun rarely shone. Then up again to a vast grey castle that seemed to grow like a shattered tree stump from the mountainside beneath it.

The eagle wheeled and circled. Far beneath them the heavy gates opened and a huge, shambling creature shuffled into the depths of the forests.

"He has gone hunting for the day," said the bird. "Now keep silence that his wife may not hear us, and we may leave safely with your lady." With a stomach-churning swoop they swung down and landed on the window ledge of the highest room in the tower.

"Calum!" Catriona screeched, jumped back, and then threw her arms around him as he landed at her feet, frozen and terrified.

They clung together, speechless with delight. It would seem that all Calum's trouble were over, but not so.

"Hush!" he warned, but it was too late. A roar rattled the window panes. The stairs shook. A bolt shot back with a crash and the huge door was flung open. Standing before them, huge, stinking and ugly, was the giant's wife.

"You thocht to rescue the lassie did you?" she howled. "We'll soon see aboot that, I'll have you in a stewpot for Himself in no time, young man."

"Hang about a minute," Calum protested as a huge hand reached out. "Let's not be so hasty. You can't eat me before we've been introduced. The name is Calum."

"Pleased to meet you I'm sure," grunted the giantess flashing him a horrible toothless smile. "You'll be right nice in a pot wi' carrots and onions."

"Just . . . just let me tell you a wee story," said Calum dodging under a chair. "You see, me and Catriona are very much in love."

"Is that a fact?" She poked for him with a wooden spoon the size of an oar.

"Very much," sighed Catriona, then she sniffed and started to cry.

"Och, for goodness sake stop it!" wheezed the giantess, reaching for a filthy handkerchief the size of a tablecloth.

"And we're to be married," said Calum. "I've booked the church. My Grannie's made the cake and the most beautiful dress for Catriona."

"Beautiful," sniffed Catriona. "All white, with pink roses."

The giantess burst into tears and blew her nose so loudly the eagle was blown off his perch on the window-ledge. She was a romantic, kind-hearted soul, and deeply touched by the story.

"Tell you what," she gulped in the end, "as a special favour, I'll let you go . . ."

"Och thanks, Your Hugeness," gasped Catriona and Calum.

"But on wan condition. You must get me the only thing I've always wanted. I've told Himself about it often enough, but does he listen? Not him . . ."

"I'll get it for you, whatever it is," said Calum. "Just tell me quick, before he gets back."

"A necklace," simpered the giantess. "A great big pearl necklace. The sort of thing that will go with my best frock, and make me look really lovely. D'ye know whit ah mean?" She patted her greasy, grey hair and giggled horribly.

Calum nodded, stunned into silence. Where would he ever find such a necklace.

"Bring me that and ye'll get yir wee lassie back, but not before. Do you hear me?" Calum was already hanging like grim death around the neck of the eagle and heading for home.

But there was no such necklace to be found, and even if there had been, where was he to find the money to buy it?

Calum was wandering along the beach late one evening pondering these problems, when there came a squeaking at his feet. He turned, and there were the otters playing in the pools left by the turning tide. Often enough before he had sat and watched them at their games and listened to their problems, now they listened to his.

"Pearls, is it?" squeaked the biggest otter. "Ah well, you have to talk to the sea people for that. You've helped us often enough in the past, I don't see why we shouldn't help you now." Before Calum had time to say another word, the otters were all about him, dragging him into the water.

Down and down they went, falling through the crystal green water, far deeper than Calum had ever swum before, but still the otters pulled him down until they came to the black mouth of an undersea cave. Through the tunnel he spun, twisting and turning, until he found himself pulled to his feet in a vast world of light and colour, where vaults of pink and white coral glowed in the green sea light, sparkling with precious stones.

The otters led Calum on to the innermost cave, and there

in the Presence Chamber where the King of the Sea held court with his daughter, Calum told his story again.

The King listened with understanding, for Calum was known to him as a man of gentleness who had helped many sea creatures in the past.

"For a friend of our people I have pearls, and to spare. Go, fetch me such a necklace," he ordered, and trusting only his daughter he gave her the key to his treasure cavern.

It would seem that Calum's troubles were over, but not so.

The Sea King's daughter was beautiful, but wilful. What she fancied she would have, and she fancied Calum. And so it was that she combed out her green hair, and returned with a necklace of pearls, each as large as a fist, and shining like the moon. In her other hand, though, she brought a deep shell filled to the brim with a wine known only to the fairy folk, a wine to delight the senses and steal the memory, the Elixir of Enchantment.

"Here are your pearls," she said. "But wait you now, the journey back is long and hard. Stay a while, quench your thirst, and drink and eat with us."

Calum drank, and with his thirst went the memories of his past life, his lost love, the giantess and her pearls.

So he would have lived happily enough, for ever and a day, had it not been for Catriona.

She sat spinning in the tower room, week after week, until the giant had scarves, tunics, pullovers and trousers enough to last him forever, but still there was no sign of Calum. Gradually the giantess began to believe he would never come back and she allowed Catriona to come downstairs and sit with her in the hall.

One hot summer day Catriona begged to be allowed out of the castle to walk by the bank of the river at the foot of the mountain and there it was she met the salmon, and the two got chatting. She spun her wool, and he spun her a yarn or two concerning his travels around the oceans of the world. She told him the story of Calum and his quest for the pearls.

"But I fear he has forgotten me," she sighed.

"I will find him for you," said the salmon. "But give me some token that I may remind him of you." Catriona broke off a piece of the white wool she was spinning and tied it around the fish, who leapt flashing and spinning in the sunlight and vanished off down the river toward the sea.

In time he found the otters who remembered well how they had helped Calum. In time he found his way to the deep sea cave, through the dark tunnel and into the vaulted halls of coral. And not a moment too soon, for there was the Sea King, with all his court about him, preparing for the marriage of his daughter to Calum the fisherman.

A flick of his tail, a twist of his fin and the salmon circled Calum, flashing silver in the green light. But around him was tied the piece of white wool, a faint memory from the world that Calum had left behind. He reached out, and as his fingers untied the knot, the fairy spell was broken.

Back to his memory came Catriona, the giantess and the quest for the pearls which now hung about his own neck as wedding finery.

It was in vain that the Sea King's daughter wept, in vain that her father tried to plead. Calum must return to his own lost love. He threw his arms about the salmon and together they swept from the cave, up through the tumbling seas toward the land where the fresh water of the river mingled with the tides.

On and on they went, past the nets at the river mouth, skirting deep pools where men cast lines to catch the great fish, leaping waterfalls, on up the mountain side to the pool beneath the massive grey castle on the cliff.

Calum climbed from the water and hid in the bushes until he saw the giant lumber off to the hunting. Then quick as a flash he was through the gate before it swung shut, striding across the courtyard into the hall, where Catriona and the giantess sat on either side of the fire.

"A promise is a promise," he declared. "I have brought you the pearls." He took the rope of huge beads from around his neck and threw it at the feet of the giantess who seized them joyfully.

"Awa' wi' ye. Quick noo, afore Himself gets back," she said, draping the pearls around her neck. She spat on her filthy handkerchief and tried to rub a clean spot on the mirror high above their heads.

"Lovely!" she said, arranging the beads beneath her chins. "Pure dead brilliant!" And then a sudden thought struck her.

"Here, would you let me come to yir wedding in my best frock and . . ."

But Calum and Catriona never heard her. They were off down to the river and home.

Michael Scott And The Wee Imp O' Hell

Anyone will tell you that there are some days when, no matter how hard you try, you just cannot get on with the work. Roll up your sleeves to do a washing and the telephone rings. Pile all the furniture into the middle of the room to redecorate, and who do you find on the doorstep but your Auntie Bella, who hasn't been to see you for ten years. Set out to tidy the garden and some neighbour will pop his head over the fence to ask what you're doing.

It's surprising how often that happens. Most times the interruptions are pleasant ones. A telephone call you've been waiting for, a happy family surprise visit, or a chance to catch up on a good gossip. But sometimes – just sometimes – the interruptions are rather more of a nuisance, and more than a wee bit sinister. Like the time Michael Scott had all the trouble.

It was a while back now, and most people have forgotten him, but there was a day when the name of Michael Scott was known – and maybe even feared – thoughout Scotland. He lived in a time before cars and tarmac roads and concrete houses put us all into straight lines and square boxes where everything has to have a reason, and every reason has to be a sensible one.

In Michael's day folk were very canny indeed about the dark corners, both in their homes and their minds. They made a point of saying "Good day" when crossing a Fairy Bridge, always left out a bowl of milk at night for who knows what might be passing, and generally took a great deal more heed of the trees and flowers and the unseen lives around them than we do now.

If they had some sort of small problem they took it to a fortune teller, or a herbal doctor. If the problem needed more powerful treatment, they took their courage in both hands, and went to Michael Scott. Not that there was anything really frightening about Michael, but you just never knew.

He was a strange man. Big and strong, he could have been old, or young, or both, hard to say. He lived alone, except for a strange assortment of animals, at least some of which were alive, and he did not suffer fools gladly. If he felt that you were wasting his time he could be terrifyingly rude, roaring oaths in a voice that rolled like thunder. But other times, with a child or hurt animal, he was soft and gentle as the swans on Glenluce bay. There is just no telling with a wizard, and that is exactly what Michael Scott was, a man with powers of magic beyond anything you or I could imagine possible.

And he used those powers well, like the time the Devil let loose in Scotland the plague whose name men hardly dared to whisper, the dreaded Black Death itself. It took all Michael Scott's power and guile to trap that terrible sickness and shut it tight in the vault of a holy place where the Devil would never get at it again. But succeed he did, and the Devil never forgave him for it. He was forever thinking up ways to get his own back.

Now it happened one time that he was sitting there in Hell, surrounded by his wee imps, who were poking and prodding and teasing the poor sinners, and, always on the look-out for talent, he noticed there was one particularly irritating wee imp. He just seemed to have learned the right way to make a thorough nuisance of himself.

"He'll do," thought the Devil, and with a flash and a bang the wee imp was delivered to Michael Scott's doorstep to see what mischief he could create in the great man's life.

The wee imp had a rare time. When the wizard put on a kettle to boil a cup of tea, you could be sure it was tipped into the fire and the flames turned to hissing ash. When he retired to his room at night, having put the cat out, and fed the bats and toads, you could be sure he would find the sheets tumbled and dirty, and the odd hedgehog or two where you least expected it. Whatever job Michael Scott turned his hand

to, that wee imp was there before him, turning things tapsal-teerie and enjoying every minute of it.

Enough was enough. The little creature would have tried the patience of a saint and Michael Scott, whatever else he might be, was no saint.

"Look here you," says he one day. "Do you never get bored with these daft antics."

"Naw," says the wee imp. "Ah love it!"

"Well could you not go and try it somewhere else?"

"Naw," says the wee imp. "The Big Man says I was to work on you."

"Aye, and you're working well!" says Michael. "You must be fair worn out by now. Sit down and we'll have a wee cuppa."

"Och no," says the wee imp, but just to be friendly, he sat down anyway.

"You know," says Michael Scott, passing the chocolate biscuits. "It's not much of a job for a wee fella with your kind of brains. Could you not find something better?"

"Naw, naw. I've to stay here. I'm allocated to you and that's it. Forever. Lifetime contract."

"Och, you've a fair bit ahead of you then," says the wizard, stretching out in his favourite armchair. "I've a few hundred years to go yet. Is there no way you can get out at all?"

"Well – only the one," says the wee fella. "An' you couldnae dae it."

"Do what?" says the crafty wizard leaning forward quietly.

"Set me an impossible task. If I cannae dae it, I have to leave you," says the wee imp. And then he blushed. "But here, you're not supposed to know that."

"Ah, but I do now," says Michael. "And what do you say we try it. Just for fun, eh?"

"Aye, aw right then." To be honest the wee imp was bored, and quite confident he could handle anything the wizard might throw at him.

"Right," says the wizard, "let me think. Do you know the River Tweed that runs fast and free across the Border hills to Berwick?"

"I do that," says the wee imp. "Many's the night I've got my hooves wet, caught in a flood. Yon's wild water, whiles."

"Just so," says Michael. "And nowhere is it wilder than down by Kelso town. The good people and the council have tried for years to build a dam that would protect their land, and not a few have lost their lives trying."

"Aye, so what then?"

"So you do it," said the wizard. "In one night – by yourself."

"Easie peasie!" says the wee imp, and off he vanished in a puff of smoke. The big wizard put the kettle on, lit a pipe and sat back to enjoy his first peaceful cup of tea in weeks.

Next morning though in comes the wee imp, and slosh goes the porridge pot, all over the fire.

"You're back," sighs the wizard.

"Ah am that," says the wee imp. "Built the dam, just like you said. Nae bother."

"Aye, sure, you're a clever wee man right enough," says Michael. "Draw up a chair. Breathe on that bread to make some toast then we'll think about the next task."

"Great," says the wee imp. "But try and make it a hard one this time wull ye? Ah'm really enjoying this."

"Hills," said Michael Scott after thinking into his mug of tea for a while. "What they need round here are more hills."

"How's that?" says the wee imp, tilting back on his chair, a most irritating habit.

"They're always arguing about the good grazing on the sunny side . . ."

"Ah LIKE arguments," says the wee imp.

". . . and how some folk never get the chance to put their sheep on it," said the wizard, ignoring him. "Because there is only the one, Eildon Hill . . ."

"Aye, so what then?" says the wee imp, impatient to get on with it.

"Split the hill into three," says the wizard. "So they all have a sunny side. And do it in one night – by yourself."

"Is that all?" says the wee imp, and off he vanished in a puff of smoke. The big wizard sat down to enjoy a quiet snooze and read his paper in peace.

Next morning, Michael Scott was hardly awake when in storms the wee imp, crashing and banging round the bedroom like a hurricane.

"You're back," yawns the big wizard.

"Ah am that," says the wee imp. "And jist look what I've

done." He pulled back the curtains. Michael opened the window and leaned out.

"In the name of goodness," he gasped.

"Naw, it wisnae that!" grinned the wee imp. "Am I not the clever one then?" The wizard took a long, hard look. Across the valley, where there had always been the one high green peak of Eildon Hill, there were now three quite distinct peaks. Even from his window he could hear the commotion down in the village as the locals gathered in the square, still arguing about what had happened in the night.

"Some folk are never happy," he grumbled, climbing back into bed.

"Good," says the wee imp, tweaking the blankets away to leave the wizard's feet sticking out, cold and white. "Suit's me fine. Go on – whit's next. Go on, go on, see whit you can think up. Bet I can dae it – staunin' on ma heid!"

"Oh no," says the wizard, pulling the blankets back. "You're far too clever for the likes of me, I'm afraid. Far too clever."

"Aw come on!" says the wee imp, really disappointed. "There must be something you can think up." Michael Scott sat up in bed, removed his red woolly nightcap, and put on his star-spangled thinking hat.

"Aye, well, maybe . . ." he pondered. "Och, but you're far too clever. You'd do that as well, no bother."

"WELL TELL ME!" said the wee imp, quite desperate to show off his talents. "Whit is it you want?"

"Just a length of rope," says the big wizard. "That's all."

"Rope? What kind of challenge is that?" The imp was quite disgusted. "Ah'll get ye any kind of rope you want. Whit is it tae be? Arabian? Chinese cord? An Indian rope trick? You name it, pal. Ah promise you, on mah mither's pointed tail, that if Ah cannae get it, ye'll be free o' me forever. But ah'll get it, nae problem."

"No, nothing fancy," says Michael. "You can get it in Scotland."

"Aw, some challenge that!"

"But it's got to be a rope made of sand . . ."

"Sand?"

". . . sand from the shore of Glenluce Bay."

"Rope? Made from the sand on the shore of Glenluce Bay?" repeated the wee imp, laughing. "Nae problem. Put the kettle on, big yin, an' I'll be back in time for tea break." He vanished with a flash and a bang.

"Show off!" muttered Michael Scott, but he put the kettle on right enough, and then took his mug of tea back to bed with the newspaper.

He spent a quiet and peaceful day, sorting through a couple of old spell books, and restocking jars of this and that in his storecupboard. He went to bed that night, still enjoying the peace and quiet, for there was no sign of the wee imp.

And in fact he never did come back again because Michael's last challenge was far too much for him.

You know what it's like some days, when you try to get on with the work and everything goes against you. It was like that for the wee imp. You see, he had forgotten about the constantly changing winds and seas of the Solway Firth and Glenluce Bay, and just as soon as he heaped the sand up to do anything with it, it blew away again, or the tide turned and washed it all out to sea.

He was a right obstinate wee creature though, and he just would not give up. He's still there to this day, struggling with the problem. You can hear him if you walk along the beach on a quiet day. Just stand a minute by the water's edge where the waves curl up onto the ridged wet sand and listen, carefully. Far behind the sound of the great ocean breathing, and the laughing gulls dancing on the wind, you can hear the wee imp, grumbling to himself.

"R-r-ropes-s-s of s-s-sand. R-r-ropes-s-s of s-s-sand!"

But you and I know he'll never make it.

You could feel sorry for him.

Almost.

Fergus And The Storyteller

Fergus was hungry, and he knew what hunger was. His father was long since dead, serving a lost cause in a needless war, and Fergus, as the oldest son, had grown up struggling to keep his mother, younger brother and two little sisters fed and warm. But it was hard, painfully hard, to watch his mother grow old and worn, and the little ones almost too weak to cry for the pains of hunger in their bellies.

He sighed and drew his worn jerkin closer around him, against the icy needles of the winter rain. He had spent all day roaming barren hillsides, hunting for a deer, a hare, even a rabbit to throw in the pot, but with no luck. Now, down off the hill, he followed the river that led to his home where he must return empty-handed to a bare table and a cold bed.

His mother, as always, made the best of it.

"You've a good heart, Fergus," she said. "And at least we will all sleep easier knowing you are safe home." She laid a few of the carefully hoarded sticks on the low fire, blew the glowing ashes to a flame, and drew up the big chair for him. But still he shivered, and the little ones cried for lack of food.

In desperation she did the only thing she could.

"Off to sleep with you bairns," she said. She tucked them all together in the big cupboard bed at the back of the cottage, covered them over with her own shawl, and told them a story of how they would awake to find fresh bread and a great pan of thick hot soup ready for them. And the way she described the taste and smell of that meal sent them to sleep happy.

She left them then and stepped out, down to the river bank where she placed a huge stone in the bottom of her biggest cooking pot and covered it with water.

"Mind your feet, Fergus," she said moving him aside to haul the pot onto the fire.

"Whatever are you doing, Mother?" he asked, astonished.

"I have promised the bairns soup, and soup they shall have," she said firmly.

"But Mother . . ."

"Away to bed with you too, laddie. You look bone weary."

Fergus shook his head sadly, and climbed to his bed in the roof of the cottage, leaving her nursing the last heat of the fire around the big pan.

As she sat dreaming into the dying flames, there came a soft chap-chapping at the door. At first she ignored it, thinking it to be the wind in the bushes. But it came again, soft and insistent, until at last, very cautiously, she opened the door and peered out into the darkness.

At first she could see nothing, and then suddenly her heart skipped a beat as she realised how close, and how still the stranger was standing. The tall, shadowy figure seemed to be wearing a long cloak, and a huge brimmed hat that hid his face.

"I seek shelter, and food, good woman." His voice was soft, with a deep, ringing power. Despite her fear she opened the door wide, and dropped a curtsey.

"There is no food here," she said as he bowed his head to enter the tiny cottage. "But the shelter beneath my roof is yours."

"No food?" The stranger smiled. "Then what is it that you have boiling in the pot?" She hesitated, but his eyes seemed to miss nothing, and what was there to hide?

"A stone," she said simply. "I promised my bairns soup and bread, and all I have is stones and water."

"Is that so?" He leaned across to peer into the pot, and as his shadow fell across it, the room was filled with the mouth watering smell of rich broth. "It would seem to me, mistress, that you have there a leg of mutton fit to feed an army."

"Merciful heavens," she whispered realising the truth of his words. "Who – or what are you?"

"A stranger, a wanderer, a travelling storyteller." He laughed again and drew up a chair to the table. "And a hungry one at that. I will have a bowl of your soup with a heel of bread from the meal kist there."

"But the kist has been empty these last months . . ." The

words died on her lips as she opened it and found herself staring at a pile of fresh, crisp brown loaves.

"The bairns," she gasped, "and Fergus! They must see this for themselves. Unless I am dreaming." The stranger, ahead of her, was already setting bowls on the table.

What a feast there was then. Fergus, his mother and the children ate and drank their fill and still there seemed no end to the bread and soup. And when they were too full to eat another scrap the stranger stirred up the fire, which seemed to burn brighter and warmer for him, and told them story after story, of kings and dragons and magical deeds.

At last as the wonderful night drew to a close, the stranger stood to take his leave. Fergus rose with him.

"There is little we can do to thank you sir," he said. "We had nothing to offer and you gave us bread and meat. Take what you will for your journey, and our prayers and blessings go with you."

"You had little to offer," agreed the stranger. "But still you gave the greatest gift of all to a complete stranger – the warmth of your hearts. Come with me now, Fergus. Set my foot on the high road, and I will give you my last gift, one to bring you joy and fortune for the rest of your days."

So Fergus led the stranger down the path, across the river by the stepping stones and up over the hill towards the road.

But as they climbed to the top of the ridge, the day grew cold and grey, and a mist came down about them, thick and swirling. Fergus turned this way and that, losing all sense of direction.

"Wait for me!" he shouted. And heard only the stranger's light mocking laughter ahead of him.

"Courage, Fergus! Have courage and follow me." The voice led on, now to this side, now to that, and Fergus stumbled across the loose stones, struggling to keep up.

Suddenly a hand reached out and he was pulled to his feet. The stranger stood, a dark shadow in the mist in front of him.

"We must part now," he said. "I to my High Road, and you down the glen . . ."

"But we are nowhere near the road . . ." The stranger held up a hand to silence him.

"Down the glen with you I say, and there you will find a castle. Enter without fear my friend, for although the castle and lands lie in thrall to a fierce giant, there are none there who will stop you. They have slept long and deep these many years, and it is for you to wake them and reap the rewards."

"But how may I do that?"

"Enter without fear, I say. And make your way through each of the rooms to the topmost tower. There you will find a princess who lies, as do the others, deep asleep. Above her head there hangs a jewel, rich and fabulous. Touch the jewel, and the princess will awaken."

"But what then?"

"What indeed? Ask for the princess, my friend." The stranger's voice faded in the mist.

"Wait, wait!" shouted Fergus reaching wildly in front of him. He tripped, rolled over and sat up to find that the mist had vanished from the mountains. Far beneath him stretched a rich green glen, and at the head of the glen on a wooded rise above a river, there stood an ancient grey castle.

Of the stranger there was no sign. Neither on the open hillside nor on the road to the glen.

Fergus clambered unsteadily to his feet and made his way down the hillside toward the castle.

Coming down off the hill the fresh wind dropped and the heat of the sun soaked through his thin jacket, as if summer had come early to the glen. The stillness of sleep hung about the ancient grey stone walls, no birds sang around the towers, and even the river whispered over the stones.

As he crossed the bridge, Fergus could see that the old wooden gates stood open and weeds grew thick between the paving stones. In the centre of the courtyard, a tree hung heavy with rich red plums. Greatly daring, he picked one and bit into the sweet, soft flesh. Then filling his pockets, he padded softly through rooms and hallways. In the guardhouse the soldiers slumped, snoring loudly. The stable boy slept, curled up in the straw. The cook lay stretched out on the kitchen table, his fingers loosely entwined on his little round belly, and in the great hall beneath the heavy curtains, finely dressed lords and ladies slumped around the table, lost in dreams.

"I must make haste," gasped Fergus, beginning to feel the spell of the place close about him, and his eyelids droop sleepily. Room by room he searched the castle, his boots becoming heavier with each step. Until finally, dragging himself up the twisting stair of the tower, he fell against the door and tumbled into a room flooded with blinding sunlight.

In the middle of the floor stood a high white bed on which lay the princess, dressed in white silk with her long dark hair spread around her. Above the bed hung a wonderful canopy of flowers made from finely twisted silver, among which precious stones glittered and sparkled throwing their brilliant colours to all the corners of the room.

"Glory!" whispered Fergus and then remembering the words of the stranger, he reached up and very gently ran his fingers along the edge of the silver canopy. It was as if he had drawn back an unseen curtain. The princess opened her eyes and sat up, reaching out a hand to him.

"Who are you, boy, and how came you here? Why do you stare so? And have you no tongue in your head? Order me a meal at once, I am hungry." Fergus helped her down from

the bed, speechless with wonder. She seemed more dazzlingly beautiful even than the sunlight. He fetched a jug of wine that stood on a side table, and placed it before her with the plums. Then as she ate and drank, he told his story.

"Indeed it is so," she said, as the memory came back to her. "The giant hated my father the king. He envied him his wealth, power, and . . ." she smiled sweetly, "his beautiful daughter."

"Indeed!" said Fergus, head over heels in love.

"But the spell can only be broken when the giant is dead."

"Tell me how I may do it," said Fergus, ready to take on the world.

"It was said by the wisest men," whispered the princess, "that the giant's life is contained in the shell of an egg, and that egg is in the possession of an old witch. If you would kill the giant, you must find the egg and shatter it. But first, you must destroy the witch."

"Then tell me where I may find her," demanded Fergus.

"At the entrance to the glen. Her cottage guards the road, that none may come or go without her knowledge. You must have come by other ways, your friend has power."

"Indeed," agreed Fergus.

He made his way back out of the sleeping castle and down the glen as the princess had instructed. In a dark little wood, where the ground lay marshy all year long, and the air hung heavy with insects, he found the ramshackle cottage.

He battered on the door, and stepped back, shocked, as it was suddenly thrown open. An ancient, filthy woman watched him warily, it was clear from her dirt-streaked face that she had been weeping.

"Good day to you, old woman," he said, as politely as he could. "What is it ails you?"

"That I cannot tell, but I feel my strength and power stolen from me," she croaked, and then she eyed him craftily. "Come stranger, you look kind enough to help an old woman. If you would only carry me into the sunlight I think all might be well again."

"No sooner said than done," said the bold Fergus, and he lifted the old woman onto his back.

"Haha!" she cackled, her arms locking viciously about his neck. "I have you now, my fine laddie, and will keep you." But love for the princess gave Fergus strength. Bracing himself he swung round and round on his feet, faster and faster.

"Go now," he shouted, snatching at the old woman's hands to loosen her grip. She flew off, landed in the fireplace, and vanished up the chimney with a vivid green flash and an ear-splitting thunderclap.

Fergus stood waiting, until his head stopped spinning, and her screams no longer rang in his ears, and then he turned his attention to the house. High and low he searched for the egg, in cupboards and beneath beds. At last he found it, wrapped in a pile of filthy rags and hidden in an empty water barrel.

"Well, well," said Fergus, lifting out the huge white shell, which shone in his hands with a strange greenish light. "We will soon see an end to this."

His hands burned, his head swam, and the air was filled with an eerie wailing. With all his strength he threw the egg and it fell, shattering into a thousand pieces, on the hearthstone of the tiny cottage. The sky blackened, there was a great roaring in the wind, the eerie wailing rose to a ringing scream of terror, and then just as it seemed his head might burst, and his teeth be shaken from his mouth, Fergus found himself lying among the ruins of the cottage. Above the shattered roof, birds sang in the trees, and the air seemed fresh and clear as it would after a summer storm.

He made his way then back along the glen road to the castle.

A blue and gold flag fluttered in the breeze high above the battlements. There was a sound of hammering as carpenters worked to repair the rotting gateway. The courtyard was bustling with happy, laughing people. In the kitchen the cook puffed at the fire, and grumbled about the pantry boys. In the hall, the princess was waiting with her father, the king, and all their courtiers.

There was feasting and rejoicing then, and great honours heaped on Fergus. Not the least of which was the hand of the princess in marriage. He brought his mother and young brother and sisters to live in the castle, and from that time, until the end of his long and happy life, he always ensured that, come what may, his gates must stand open to any passing stranger who begged a bed and food for the night.

The Seer's Stone

It is a fact, generally accepted, that there are people who are able to see beyond the world we live in, and to foretell the future. There was one such man in Scotland, three, maybe four hundred years ago. Coinneach Odhar he was known as in the Gaelic tongue which was widely spoken at that time – Dark Kenneth.

He was born on the long island of Lewis far out on the north west coast. Life on the islands is hard, even now, and at that time his parents, like the other islanders, had a sore struggle to feed and clothe themselves. They scratched a living from the poor soil of their tiny croft, and the baby's mother, Morag MacKenzie tended their few sheep, spinning and weaving the wool. Her husband spent his days fishing in the dangerous waters of the Minch. Nevertheless they were contented people and their happiness was made complete with the birth of their son.

"We must call him Kenneth, after his grandfather," said Morag's husband, for whom the ceremonies and traditions of life meant much. "He will grow to farm and fish the croft as my father and his father did before him."

But Morag Mackenzie was proud and ambitious for her

son. From the day and hour he was born she insisted that his life must be different.

And in many ways he was different, even as a tiny bairn. You see, at one time the islands had lived under Viking rule, and although by Kenneth's time they owned allegiance to the Scottish crown, the people still had the look of their marauding ancestors. They were tall and fair, their children were long-legged and blonde, with sea blue eyes.

But not the Mackenzie bairn. From the start Kenneth was smaller, dark-skinned, black haired, with eyes brown as the deep lochans on the peat moors. Where other children laughed and smiled, he was still and quiet. In him there was a distant echo of the race who had ruled the land before the Vikings. The people who had gone, leaving eerily powerful circles of standing stones on windswept hillsides, and by shady woodland streams, roughly carved altars dedicated to their Celtic gods.

The village women soon noticed the child's strange look, and were superstitious and fearful.

"He maun be a changeling," they whispered behind closed doors. "That bairn's a fairy child right enough. There's something unco wierd aboot him."

It was the opinion of all that whatever happened to the child in life, he would surely come to a bad end. But, nothing daunted, Morag Mackenzie ignored them. Her husband, however, heard the rumours too, and was afraid for his son.

"You maun stop this nonsense, Morag," he said. "Wha kens whit trouble ye may steer up, gin ye boast aboot the bairn." Morag laughed in his face.

"My son will be a great man one day," she insisted. "He will be no farmer or fisherman to soil his hands like you. I tell you, guidman, the day will come when oor son's name will be kent the length and breadth o' this land."

"Morag, Morag! Tae be a great man he would need to have some power over ither men, and, God kens a crofter's son will never have that."

Morag smiled, and answered not a word. From that day she boasted no more about her son, but still she held her dream close to her heart.

It happened the following summer that she took the sheep to the shieling on the headland above the ancient churchyard. Each winter the village folk kept their few cows and sheep indoors, then each summer, as the young grass grew lush and green, the starved animals were driven out to the sunlit pastures of the summer shieling to fatten up. While their menfolk farmed the croft or went off to the fishing, the women and their younger children left for the shieling with their animals.

On the sunlit hillside, the children played, the women with their distaffs, spun the wool they had washed and carded. And as they worked they sang, gossiped, and tended their beasts and children. And through the long white northern summer nights, they slept in the tiny shieling huts.

One night, towards Midsummer Eve, Morag lay sleepless. For days the weather had been hot and breathless, the sky burning brass and the sea a lethargic, leaden blue.

The hut was airless. She tossed and turned in her own corner, apart from the others. The soft blanket beneath her felt rough as the moorland heather, her mind's eye tumbled ceaselessly with images of the day's events. At last, she sat up in the half-dark and looked around her. By her side, her child slept, the other women and their children too lay like basking seals, breathing softly in the darkness. Morag drew her shawl about her, and lifting her distaff and some wool, she rose and crept on bare feet, feeling her way along the rough stone wall to the doorway.

The air was fresh and cool on her burning face as she pulled aside the heavy leather curtain. Drawn by the smell of the sea, a longing swept through her, and in the soft, grey half-light she picked her way down the hillside. Past the dark statues of the quietly munching cows she went, leaving the trail of her feet and skirt on the dew-silvered grass, down to the ruined kirkyard by the sea shore.

But this night was like no other. There was a tension in the air, an excitement that Morag felt deep within herself. As she walked, she felt, rather than saw, movement around her.

And yet the air was still, as if waiting. Mist hung about the hillside in soft, chilling banks. The sea waves broke on the beach, 'hush, hush, hush,' with a soft whisper of warning.

Morag, suddenly fearful of she knew not what, crouched in a corner by the kirkyard wall. Holding her breath she waited, peering into the half-dark, scarcely trusting the evidence of her eyes in the shifting light, for it seemed as if the smooth green grass above the graves had opened. The trails of mist, separating, formed themselves into shapes that came and went. The shapes took on form. The forms became men, women, and children who floated from the open graves across the hillside into the mists.

At first, shaking with terror, Morag prayed. But then seeing that the ghosts meant her no harm, she watched them come and go around her.

And gradually she realised that as the long night wore on towards morning they returned. The mist cleared and in the growing light she could see the graves, covered again, still and peaceful under their thick blanket of grass.

All but one.

One grave lay alone by the beach. She knew it well. The fallen stone was ancient and moss-covered, the carved patterns worn beyond recognition. It was the oldest, the first grave, and around the fire in the evening tales were told of the Viking princess buried there. Now, in the grey light of dawn, it alone lay open.

Morag knew with sudden certainty what she must do. It was for this she had been drawn to the kirkyard. Creeping forward, she laid her distaff across the grave, for it was said that where a distaff lay, no spirit might enter. But she knew too that the mortal who helps a spirit find rest may ask any gift in return. And so she laid down her distaff and knelt by the stone, and waited.

At last, as she drifted into sleep in the early morning light, there came a voice.

"Lift thy distaff, woman, that I may return to my grave."

Morag sat up, rubbing her eyes. But still her sight seemed blurred as if by sleep.

At her side stood a young woman, a wraith of astonishing beauty. Her long hair hung in white plaits to her waist. A silver white robe of mist and water hung about her bare seaweed tangled feet.

"Lift thy distaff, woman, I beg you." The voice was soft and pleading. But Morag denied her.

"The others have returned long since. Why then are you so late? Tell me, or my distaff stays where it is."

"I have travelled long and far," the voice came again like a soft wind through the heather, "and must rest . . . rest . . . rest . . ."

Again Morag denied her.

"Tell me from whence you come, and why?"

"Once I was young and happy," whispered the ghost. "I lived in your world of the sun's light. In my mouth was the taste of the meat and grain of the earth. Now there is only the taste of the grave . . ."

"But tell me," demanded Morag, as the voice faded.

"I was the daughter of a Viking Jarl whose ships ranged from the icy dragon lands of the north to the burning world of the southern seas. I lived in a palace, I might have married a prince, but I would not be contented, for more than anything I loved the sea, and longed to be free as the winds . . . But make haste, woman, remove thy distaff. The dawn returns, and with the first sunlight I am doomed to wander forever."

But a third time Morag denied her, and demanded to hear the story.

"Then know you that swimming I was drowned, and my body drifting on the winds and tides was found at last on this beach. Here I lie buried, but when the time of freedom

comes I must return to my home across the Northern Sea
. . . do not deny me that right, I beg you."

"I will remove my distaff, and leave you to your rest," said
Morag. "But in return I demand of you a treasure . . ."

The wraith sighed, deep and long.

"A treasure for my son, that he may grow to have power
over other men. I demand what is mine to ask and yours to
give."

"Foolish woman," sighed the wraith. "Foolish woman that
will not rest content. You shall have your son's treasure."

"And he will become a great man? His name known, and
feared, far and wide?"

"Far and wide."

"Then tell me what I must do."

"Go you to the sea," whispered the princess, her voice and
form fading in the growing light. "And walk by the water's
edge."

"And then what? Quickly, quickly!"

"Turn to face the sun and you will see at your feet a stone
. . ."

"A stone!"

"Hush, woman, there is little time. It is a smooth blue
stone, and through the stone there is a hole. Take it and
guard it well for your son."

"But what way will that make him rich," demanded Morag.
"The beach is covered with stones, there for the taking."

"That one has power," the voice was scarcely audible.
"When he is old enough, show him that he must put it to
his left eye and look through the hole and there he will see
the future. He alone will have the gift of knowing what is to
come. The lives of the poor and of the mighty will lie before
him as an open book."

"There indeed lies power," whispered Morag.

"Both good and bad," breathed the voice. "And now, I beseech you woman, bring me to my rest."

Morag lifted the distaff and as she did so her sight cleared. In the dawn light the grave at her feet lay still and green, the quiet kirkyard undisturbed as if the night had never been. She shivered, suddenly, in the cool air.

"It was a dream, surely." But then the words of the princess lingered in her mind.

"The lives of the poor and of the mighty will lie before him as an open book."

Quickly she pulled the shawl tight around her and picked her way carefully across the stones of the beach to the water's edge. And there, as the rising sun laid a path of gold across the sea, she found the stone.

Round and smooth as glass it lay in her hand. She brushed away the wet sand and saw that in her palm it was a dark shining blue. It was like no stone she had ever seen before. And so she wrapped it in her shawl, and returned to the shieling.

For many years she kept the stone hidden in a safe place and only when her son came of an age to understand, did she give it to him and tell him the story of the Jarl's daughter.

And it was as she had promised. Holding the stone to his left eye, Kenneth Mackenzie could see what was to come, both the good and the bad.

The lives of the poor and of the mighty lay before him as an open book, and power – if not happiness – was his for the taking.

Fairy Cakes

They say you should always heed a Fairy's Warning. And it's perfectly true, particularly if they happen to mention the name of Big Katie McCafferty.

She's the same Katie McCafferty who used to run Katie's Cake and Cookie Shop. They came from miles around to buy her treacle and tattie scones. They raved about her plain loaves and morning rolls. But it was the cakes that really made Katie famous. Indeed it was those cakes, and the Wee Folks' fondness for them, that made it possible for her to open the shop at all. This was the way it happened.

Wee Folk generally keep themselves to themselves and eat their own food, but if they have a particular weakness, it is that they are extremely fond of a home-made cake and are not above stealing the odd slice themselves. How often have you gone to the tin and found there's only a small piece left? Who ate the rest? Where did it go? Better not to ask sometimes. But you can be sure if you are a particularly good cake baker then the Wee Folk will get to know about it.

They knew about Katie's cakes and did their very best to get their hands on them. They used to hang around her back door, just in case she left it open a crack, but she never did, she was too clever by half. One morning though, just by chance, one of the Wee Folk happened to be passing when Big Katie had a telephone call.

"It's an order from the castle," she shouted. "The Laird's dochter's to be wed and they want a cake, twelve layers high, with silver bells and white heather. Fancy that, Donnie! I'll hae to leave you wi' Wee James for the day."

"Aye, well just tak' care yir no' too late coming hame," said her husband Donnie. "It's a lang road through the wood."

"Ach, doesn't bother me!" said Katie. "I'll take the short cut by the Fairy Hill."

"She's to bake the cake in the castle kitchen," panted the fairy who had raced back home with the news. "It'll take her all day, an' she'll gang hame late – by the short cut path round the Fairy Hill!"

In no time at all the Wee Folk had laid a plan to kidnap Katie on her way home from the castle.

"Gin we cannae steal her cakes – we'll steal the cook hersel'!" they screeched with delight. "An' she'll hae tae bide here and bake for us!"

The day of the Cake Baking arrived. After breakfast Katie packed her best apron and prepared to leave.

"Now don't you worry, I'll tak' care o' everything here," Donnie assured her. "But just mind if you're coming home by the Fairy Hill to be back by midnight, yon's no a place to linger late at nicht!"

"No fear of that!" said Big Katie, and off she went.

She spent a long, hot day in the castle kitchen. All morning the little maids ran here and there fetching and carrying, all afternoon they spent washing up behind her. She filled the castle with a mouth-watering smell of fresh-baked fruit and spices. And then, at last, when it was almost bed-time and the Laird and his family could stand it no longer, Katie threw open the kitchen door, and invited them to admire the wedding cake.

It was magnificent. They had never seen one quite like it before. Twelve layers high, each layer standing on little silver pillars and decorated with white heather and bluebells, cleverly moulded from icing. It was so beautiful even the castle cook forgot his huff and invited her to sit down for a cup of tea and a bite of supper before she left for home.

"Ah well, just a quick cuppa," said Big Katie, with an eye on the clock. "It's gone ten now, and I must be home before midnight."

But you know how it is, one cup led to another, they chatted and swapped recipes and in no time at all the kitchen clock was striking half past eleven.

Big Katie grabbed her apron and ran. Down the road from the castle she hurried, over the bridge by the mill to the cross-roads.

It was a bright moonlit night, but the long road, down through the wood looked dark and eerie with shifting shadows. To her left the short cut path up over the Fairy Hill was bright and beckoning. Stars sparkled like diamonds in the puddles, she could see every step of the way to her own little cottage down in the glen below, where Donnie had left a light in the window.

"Ach there's no harm can come to me here," she thought. "I'll just chance it."

But the hill seemed strangely steeper with every step she took, and as she climbed a great tiredness came over her, so that by the time she was half-way up she was gasping for breath.

"I doubt but I'll hae to sit down here for a wee rest," she said stretching out on the grass, and in no time at all she had fallen into a deep sleep.

It was the moment the Wee Folk had been waiting for.

Quick as a flash they seized her. She tossed and turned fitfully in her sleep hearing screams and giggles as if in a dream, and opening her eyes found herself in a huge dimly lit green cave. The laughter came from strange little creatures who seemed to melt in and out of the tree roots around her.

"Well, mercy on us!" she gasped, realising what had happened. "Whatever am I doing here?"

"Yir here to mak' oor cakes," screeched the little voices. "An' the only wey ye'll get hame is if we tak' ye."

"An' we'll never dae that!" They danced round Big Katie giggling wildly.

"Well, this is a pretty pickle I'm in," she said to herself. "What am I to do, I wonder?" Seeing there was no way of escaping, she sighed, and put on her apron.

"She's going to bake us a cake!" The Wee Folk danced a mad reel. "She's going to bake us a cake."

"Aye, but there's a wee something missing. You've no flour," said Big Katie, searching along the shelves of the fairy kitchen. "You'll have to fetch mine from the cottage." The words were hardly out of her mouth when a fairy was off and back, his wings flapping furiously.

"Here you are," he said. "Now ye can dae it."

"Right enough," said Big Katie. "But – there's a wee something missing. I need six eggs. You'll have to fetch mine . . ." The words were hardly out of her mouth when a fairy was off and back, his wings flapping furiously.

"Six eggs," he said, placing them on the table.

"Aye, that's true," said Big Katie searching around. "But there's still a wee something missing. It'll be a very dull cake without the sugar. You'll have to . . ." The words were hardly out of her mouth when a fairy was off and back, his wings flapping furiously.

"Sugar," he said, thumping it down on the table. "Now will you make the cake?"

"Make the cake! Bake the cake!" the others chanted leaping up and down, frantic with excitement.

"Aye, right," she said. "But if it's one of my SPECIAL cakes you want . . ."

"It is! It is!"

". . . there's a wee something missing. One of you will have to fetch my spice jar, it's on the dresser . . ." The words were hardly out of her mouth when a fairy was off and back, his wings flapping furiously.

"Is there anything else?" he gasped, flopping at her feet with the jar.

"Well now – there's milk . . ." Off went another fairy.

". . . and butter. And I think that's just about it," said Big Katie, counting out the ingredients on the kitchen table.

"Make the cake! Bake the cake!" shouted the Wee Folk breathlessly. "Hurry, hurry!"

"Well I would," said Big Katie. "But – there's just a wee

something missing. You don't have a baking bowl big enough, you'll have to fetch mine from . . ." The words were hardly out of her mouth when two fairies were off and back, carrying the bowl between them.

"That's more like it," said Big Katie and she tipped in the flour, and sugar, and eggs, and milk, and spices all ready to mix together. The fairies crowded around her, their tongues hanging out.

"Em – there's just a wee something missing," she said.

"Oh no!" groaned the fairies.

"You don't expect me to stir it with that silly wee spoon do you? You'll find mine . . ." The words were hardly out of her mouth when a fairy was off and back, with the wooden spoon.

84

"Just the ticket," said Big Katie, and she set to work, mixing the cake.

Slurp, slurp, slurp, slurp, went the spoon in the cake mix.

And then she stopped.

"It's no use. There's just a wee something missing."

"Whit now?" they moaned.

"It's the dog."

"The dog?"

"The dog. I like to have him lying at my feet snoring, it kind of gives me a beat for the mixing."

"Aye, right, the dog," sighed the fairies and two of them set off to drag back a very unwilling dog, who bit and snapped and snarled.

"Lie down and go to sleep," said Big Katie, when they finally got him into the Fairy Hill. The dog lay at her feet, and fell asleep.

Snore, snore, snore, went the dog.

Slurp, slurp slurp, went Big Katie, mixing the cake, soft and moist and brown.

And then she stopped.

"It's no use," she sighed. "There's just a wee something missing."

"Oh no, not again!" sighed the fairies.

"My cat."

"Your cat?"

"Every time I bake a cake he's there, purring at my feet, it just doesna' seem right without him, you'll have to . . ."

"Aye, right, the cat," sighed the fairies, and two of them set off to drag back a very unhappy cat, spitting and scratching and fighting.

"Lie down and go to sleep," said Big Katie, when they finally got back to the Fairy Hill and the cat lay at her feet and fell asleep.

Purr, purr, purr, went the cat.

Snore, snore, snore, went the dog.

Slurp, slurp, slurp, went Big Katie with the wooden spoon.

And then she stopped.

"Don't tell us," howled the fairies. "There's a wee something missing."

"It's the baby," said Big Katie. "He's cutting teeth, and I'm that worried about him." It took four fairies to drag the baby's cot back to the Hill and by the time they got him there, he was wide awake and howling.

"Waaaaa, waaaaa, waaaaa," screamed wee James.

"Oh, wheeshie whee!" crooned Big Katie.

Snore, snore, snore, went the dog.

Purr, purr, purr, went the cat.

Slurp, slurp, slurp, went the wooden spoon.

"What a din!" howled the fairies, stuffing their fingers in their ears.

Big Katie stopped mixing.

"Tell you what," she shouted. "There's a wee something missing!" She could hardly make herself heard above the row. "Away and fetch my husband. He'll keep the bairn quiet."

Donnie was a big man. It took eight of the fairies to drag him away with his slippers and his newspaper.

"Whit in the name of goodness is going on?" he shouted when they dumped him beside Big Katie. "That hoose is like a fairground tonight, what with all the coming and going . . ."

"Wheesht," she whispered. "Just do as I say and we'll be all right." She nodded to him to stand on the dog's tail.

"Owowowowow," howled the dog, louder than ever. The cat shot up, screeching and spitting. Wee James, screamed at the top of his voice.

The fairies rolled about the floor, howling in agony and begging Katie to stop the noise. But Big Katie ignored them, and clattered the spoon round the bowl.

Slurp, slurp, slurp.

And then she stopped.

"It's ready to bake," she said. The fairies sighed with relief. "But – there's a wee something missing." They screamed and moaned.

"You'll have to fetch my big baking tin . . ." she shouted above the din. Two fairies trudged out, and were back an hour later, rolling the big silver tin between them.

"Bake the cake! Make the cake!" the Wee Folk whispered hoarsely, as Big Katie tipped the mix into the tin. "Is that it ready now?"

"Well, yes," said Big Katie. "But . . ."

The Wee Folk rolled around the cave in a howling green bundle.

"Your oven's far too wee for my big cake tin, I can only cook it if you take me . . ." The words were hardly out of her mouth when four fairies grabbed her, another two took the cake tin.

"And don't forget Donnie, and the baby, and the dog, and cat and . . ."

So the Wee Folk spent the rest of that night flapping backwards and forwards between the Fairy Hill and Big Katie's cottage, and didn't she laugh at their faces when they realised that she had tricked them into taking her back home again. You never saw such a miserable bunch of fairies.

In fact they looked so miserable she took pity on them and promised to bake the cake after all. When it was cool, she covered it with lemon icing and took it back up the road to the Fairy Hill.

"Anybody there?" she called, but the only sound to be

heard was a faint snoring from deep beneath the earth, so she left the cake and went off back home again.

But that was not the end of the story. Whatever else the Wee Folk do, they will not take something for nothing, so that the very next morning Big Katie found a bag of gold coins on her doorstep. Pinned to the bag there was a note ordering a chocolate cake for the following week. Then after that it was a cream sponge, a strawberry gateau, a green birthday cake. Something different every week.

So you see that was how Big Katie McCafferty was able to make enough gold to open her own wee Cake and Cookie shop, and why you should always listen to a Fairy Warning. They know when they're beaten.

Rashiecoat

There was a king once, had an only daughter. When she came of an age to be married her father looked around for a suitable husband. The princess was determined that she would have only a prince, and one who was young, handsome and rich at that. There was just such a prince living in the neighbouring kingdom, but he had let it be known that on no account would he marry some empty-headed princess, and certainly not the daughter of a king who was rather short of money.

So the princess and her father had to look elsewhere, and his eye soon fell on one of his courtiers. The man was nobody's idea of a handsome husband, short, fat, balding and – let's be honest – he had bandy legs. But all the same he was possessed of vast wealth, many fine houses, land and servants. The king himself being none too rich, could of course foresee that there would be considerable advantage in having his daughter married off so comfortably.

The princess, however, felt very differently. She had no wish at all to become the wife of an old man, and wept long and bitterly, stamped her feet, and threw tantrums and teacups, but all to no purpose.

"You'll do as you're told," said her father, and that was that. Or so he thought.

One morning the princess was sitting under a tree by the river, weeping yet again.

"Hoot, wumman," screeched a voice at her ear. "Whit wey are ye makin' a' this fuss?" The princess stopped crying and stared. Standing over her was the old woman who cared for the hens. She was an ancient, wrinkled creature, who seemed so frail she might blow off like a feather on the next breeze. But she had bright black eyes that pierced straight into the princess, demanding an answer to her question.

"It's my father," wailed the princess. "He would have me married off to a rich old man, and I cannot stand him! Oh what'll become of me? What'll I do?"

"A rich old man?" cackled the hen-wife. "That doesnae sound too bad tae me. My dochter wouldna say no, gin he

offered tae marry her!" The princess howled louder than ever. The old hen-wife's daughter was uglier than a troll.

"He's ancient, near as old as you!" She covered her face with her hands, and rocked back and fore, crying bitterly.

"Hmphm!" sniffed the old hen-wife indignantly. "Thanks verra much, I'm sure. But I still don't see whit a' the fuss is aboot. Ye just have tae sae ye winna tak' him . . ."

"What do you think I've been DOING for weeks!"

"Will ye LISTEN tae me, just a meenit. Yir a princess, aren't ye? So yir expectit tae be a wee bittie difficult, sometimes. Well then, mak' demands. Say ye winna tak' him until they gie ye a coat o' the finest beaten gowd."

"A coat of beaten gold?"

"Aye. Why no', it's just the verra thing for a princess. And besides it'll tak' yir faither a wee whilie to find that much gold." The old hen wife gave the princess a cunning wink.

"Aye right enough," said the princess. "Why not?" So she went to her father.

"Father," said she. "I have been thinking over what you said, and I've decided if I'm to be wed, I'll have to be dressed as a king's daughter should be."

"Anything, anything, my precious," promised the king.

"In that case," said the princess. "I want a coat of the very finest beaten gold."

"Gold?" said the king faintly. "You wouldn't settle for . . ."

"No gold, no wedding," said the princess stamping her foot. She took a deep breath ready to throw another tantrum.

"You'll have your coat," sighed the king, and the princess smiled, thinking she would have a long wait.

But the king sent word to the elderly courtier who wished to marry the princess. He agreed willingly to provide half the gold, and together they scoured the length and breadth of the kingdom to find the cleverest goldsmiths. Craftsmen came from miles away to work on the coat of beaten gold. Day and night for seven months the ringing of their little hammers could be heard in the palace workshops. And all the while the king and the wealthy suitor pressed the princess to agree a date for the wedding. She smiled sweetly and shook her head.

"Wait until I have my coat of beaten gold," she said brushing down her long golden hair and dreaming of handsome princes and fine weddings.

But sooner than she had expected the coat was ready. And what a wonder it was to be sure. Fashioned from thousands of tiny golden scales, it seemed to be made of the sunlight that sparkled on the river. As the princess turned and twirled before the mirror the coat caught the light, glinting like the wee darting trout that played in the deep pools beneath the waterfall.

"Wonderful!" breathed the king, admiring his beautiful daughter.

"Right enough," wheezed the old suitor. "It's as good as money in the bank."

The princess threw off the coat, and ran down to the river where she sat crying.

"Whit's the trouble this time?" sighed the old hen wife, coming across her.

"What am I to do?" gulped the princess. "They've given me a coat of beaten gold, and now I must set a date for the wedding. But he's such an old grey curmudgeon. Oh . . . what am I to do?"

"Stop greeting for a start," said the old hen wife. "It mak's yir nose a' red." The princess sniffed and dried her eyes.

"I tell ye whit," said the old hen wife. "It seems that the gold was jist that wee bit too easy. We'll hae tae think of somethin' mair difficult." She stood and scratched a bit, and watched her hens.

"Here's whit tae dae," she said. "Awa' tae yir faither and tell him ye'll no' be merrit until they gie ye a coat made o' feathers o' a' the birds o' the air."

"All the birds of the air?"

"Aye. That'll no' be as easy tae come by as the gowd I'm thinking." The princess went back to her father.

"Father," said she. "I've been thinking over what you said, and I've decided if I'm to be wed, I'll have to be dressed as a king's daughter should be."

"But you have the coat of gold?" said the king. "And it cost a fortune!"

"Aye, but money's not everything," said the princess. "I want something that nobody else has."

"Anything! Anything, my little dumpling!" promised the king.

"I want a coat made of feathers from all the birds of the air." There was a long silence.

"Feathers!" said the king faintly. "You wouldn't settle for . . ."

"No feathers, no wedding," said the princess, stamping her foot and taking a deep breath.

"You'll have your coat," sighed the king, and the princess smiled, thinking it would take a very long time.

But the old suitor was not to be beaten. He owned farms the length and breadth of the kingdom, and sent out word to his men that each one was to take a bag of his finest corn and scatter it on the ground. Then they were to cry to all the birds.

"Each bird tak' up a grain and pit doon a feather.

Each bird tak' up a grain and pit doon a feather."

Sure enough, each bird did as it was bid, and by the end

of a year and a day the men turned up at the castle, each with his bag of feathers.

And then the work really began. The king and the elderly suitor sent for tailors and dressmakers. They came from all over the kingdom, from France and Italy and even from England, and they worked day and night for another twelvemonth to make a coat from the feathers.

At the end of twelve months and a day the coat was presented to the princess. And what a wonder it was to be sure. Around the hem was a band of deep blue, like the farthest depths of a summer sky, or the flash of a kingfisher dipping down the river pools. Across the shoulders the coat glowed, rich and dark with specks of golden light, like the stars on an autumn night, or the speckle of a starling's wing. Around her pretty face was a thick collar of white swansdown, picked out with a band of deep red from the robin's breast, like the sun on a winter's day. As she moved, the coat floated about the princess, so light and delicate it hung.

"Magnificent," whispered the king, who had never seen his daughter look so beautiful.

"Not bad at all," croaked the old man. "Despite the fact that it cost a lot of corn. It'll dae fine for a dressing goon wance we're merrit." The princess threw off the coat and ran down to the river, where she sat crying.

"Whitever's the matter noo?" screeched the hen wife, coming across her.

"They've given me a fine coat of feathers," moaned the princess. "And there's nothing for it. I must set a date for the wedding. What's to be done, hen wife?"

"Weel, ye can stop that yowling for a start," said the old woman. "Ye're like a parcel o' cats in a back yard." The princess swallowed hard, and stopped crying. The old woman sat staring at the river bank, her beady eyes half shut. Suddenly she jumped up.

"I huv it!" she said. "Ye'll gang back tae yir faither and tell him ye willna be merrit unless ye hae a coat made o' rashies."

"Rushes? You mean the reeds by the river bank there?"

"Aye. The auld yin will maybe think ye're a wee bit daft and no' want to get merrit efter a'." The princess was doubtful, but anything was worth a try.

"Father," said she. "I've been thinking about what you said, and I have decided that if I'm to be wed, it must be in a dress made of rushes."

"Rushes? You mean rushes from the river bank?"

"Rushes from the river bank," insisted the princess as she wandered off, barefoot, clutching and sniffing a bundle of rushes as if they had been the most beautiful bouquet of flowers. "And I'll have a pair of slippers to match." There was gossip in the castle.

"I doubt the poor wee lass is a bit touched with all this nonsense," they laughed, and nicknamed her Rashiecoat. But the old suitor was not in the least bit bothered. He was maybe a wee bit touched himself.

The king sent out men from the palace to cut bundles of rushes, and the young woman who darned the palace socks sat down to weave a coat and slippers for the princess.

By the next evening they were ready, and what a wonder they were to be sure. The coat was soft and green, and hanging about it was the breath of the woods and fields, the fresh mysterious smell of the living earth. The princess turned and twisted before the mirror, and her long golden hair tumbled down her coat, like the sunlight on the leaves along the river bank.

The king was speechless.

"Aye," wheezed the old man, who was fast loosing patience. "That'll dae fine tae get merrit in. We'll hae the wedding in the morn, and nae mair o' yir whigmaleeries!"

But the princess would have none of it. That night, while everyone slept she bundled together her coat of gold, coat of feathers and the coat of rushes, and waiting until it was dark, she put on an old dress and cloak, tied up her long hair in a scarf, tiptoed down the back stairs and ran away.

There was consternation in the palace, a proclamation went out that anyone who saw the princess must notify the authorities, but she never looked back.

She walked for miles, through nights and days, through towns and villages, by rivers and moorland. Here and there she stopped at an isolated cottage and was able to beg some bread or meat. The country folk felt sorry for the pretty little girl, poorly dressed and dragging her heavy bundle, and they let her do a day's work to earn a bed for the night and a bite to eat.

After many days she found she had crossed over into the neighbouring kingdom, and came to the king's castle, where she begged once more for food and shelter. The servants, seeing her clothes all mud-spattered and torn, made fun of her. But the cook, being a kind-hearted soul, took her in.

"Get back tae yir work, ye lazy limmers," she shouted, swinging at them with the frying pan. Then turning to the princess she smiled. "Come awa' intae the kitchen, lass, and dinna mind that lot. They hae as much sense among them as ye'll find in a haggis bag!" She took the little princess into the kitchen, sat her in a warm corner with a bowl of soup, and offered to let her stay if she would work as a kitchenmaid.

And so she did. The little princess forgot her tantrums. She stopped throwing teacups and washed them up instead. She worked hard from morning till night, scrubbing floors, clean-

ing vegetables and sweeping out the kitchen fire, and at night she slept on her bundle of coats by the chimney corner.

Now it happened that on Sunday morning everyone in the castle went to church, and the little princess was left behind to cook the dinner. She was sitting on the kitchen stool, peeling an enormous pile of potatoes, when suddenly the door burst open, as if blown by a great gust of wind, and there before her stood a wee man in a green tunic.

"Awa' wi' ye tae the kirk, Rashiecoat," he said. "Pit oan yir coat o' beaten gowd, and gang tae the kirk. Hurry noo."

"I cannot do that," said the princess. "There's the dinner to cook."

"Never fear," said the wee man. "I'll see to that. Jist you dae as yir tellt noo." So Rashiecoat washed her face, brushed out her long golden hair, put on her coat of beaten gold, and went off to the church.

"And mind yir back afore the ithers!" called the wee man after her.

The little princess walked into the kirk in her beautiful golden coat, and suddenly it seemed as if the sunlight hung round her lighting the old grey stones with a warmth they had never known. A whisper went round the pews. Nobody could remember ever having seen her before, and the king's son stared in astonishment. By the end of the first hymn he had decided that he must talk to this beautiful creature, and by the end of the sermon he had decided that come what may he would marry no other.

Rashiecoat paid no attention to him, but only tossed back her hair and slipped away at the end of the service, back to the castle kitchen, where the wee man had the dinner all ready. She hid her golden coat in its bundle by the fireside, and wrapped her hair up in a scarf, so that by the time the cook and the other servants came back she sat, quiet as a mouse, listening to all their talk about the lassie who had captured the heart of the prince.

The following Sunday, Rashiecoat was again left to make the dinner, and again the wee man came to visit.

"Ye maun pit oan yir coat o' feathers the day, Rashiecoat," he said. "An' off tae the kirk wi' ye. Quick noo or ye'll be late." Rashiecoat washed her face, brushed out her long golden hair, put on her coat of feathers and went to the kirk.

She walked down the aisle as they sang the first hymn, and the feather coat floated about her, so lightly it hung on her shoulders. Her pretty little face, framed by the swansdown collar, was so appealing that the king's son was fairly demented with love, and could scarcely take his eyes off her. But Rashiecoat turned up her nose, and slipped out while he had his head bowed during the last prayer. Although he hunted high and low, he could find her nowhere.

Hiding her feather coat by the fireside, the little princess once again prepared to serve the dinner. And as she worked, she listened quietly while the cook and servants talked about the wonderful coat of feathers, and the beautiful girl who had captured the heart of the prince.

On the third Sunday, Rashiecoat was sweeping up the hearth when the wee man came again.

"Guidsakes, lassie," he squeaked. "Pit oan yir coat o' rashes. Ye'll never get there in time." Rashiecoat laughed, washed her face, and put on the coat and slippers made of green rushes. Her golden hair tumbled down over her shoulders, and her beauty was quite enchanting.

"If it was not that she's come to a Christian kirk," whispered the prince, "I would swear yon lass was the Queen of Elfland herself."

He watched her carefully all through the service, and at the end, during the last prayers, as Rashiecoat slipped quietly from her place, he followed, and caught her arm.

"Wait!" he said. "I must speak with you ..." But Rashiecoat turned her back on him, and hurried off across the churchyard, into the trees, leaving one of her tiny green slippers in the long grass.

"Let it be known," declared the prince, desperate to find his love, "throughout the length and breadth of this kingdom, that the lass whose foot fits the slipper will be the one I'll take for my bride."

All of the fine ladies of the court tried on the tiny green slipper, but not one of them had feet as small as Rashiecoat. The prince sent his men out to hunt high and low, through towns, villages and farmsteads, but nowhere did they find a lady who could wear the tiny slipper.

They came at last to the home of Rashiecoat's father, in the neighbouring kingdom, and the old hen-wife, hearing the tale of the slipper decided that here at last was a chance to marry off her ugly daughter. The girl, ugly as a troll, was dressed up in her best clothes and forced to pinch and squeeze her large foot into the tiny slipper. It may well be that she even had to cut off a toe to make it fit, but however she did it, the slipper seemed to fit, so they took her back to the prince.

"Would you have me marry with that ill-gotten creature!" he gasped. "She's no' the lassie I saw in the kirk."

The hen-wife's daughter smiled a horrible smile, showing all her blackened teeth, and tossed her greasy tangled hair.

"Ah weel, sir," she wheezed coyly, "Ye did promise tae marry the lass that could wear yir bonny wee slipper, and there's nae doot but it fits." She waved a knobbly leg in front of him, and there, sure enough was the slipper.

Very unwillingly the prince took the hen-wife's ugly daughter up on his horse. Very unwillingly he rode back to his castle, trying to ignore the pointing fingers, and muffled

laugher in the streets as he passed. But on the way back, as
he passed by the kirkyard, there was a wee man dressed in
green, sitting on a stone and singing to himself.

"Nippit foot an' clippit foot,
Ahint the king's son rides.
But bonny foot and pretty foot,
In your ain kitchen lies."

Then the king's son looked at the little green slipper again,
and saw that the hen-wife's ugly daughter seemed to have
chopped off a toe to make it fit.

"Away home with you," he said, dumping her on the grass
and taking back the slipper. "I knew you were never my lass
at all."

The laughter of the wee man, and the screeching of the
hen-wife's daughter rang in his ears as he rode fast as his
horse would carry him, back to the castle, and there, sure
enough, just as the wee man had said, he found Rashiecoat.
She was sitting by the fire, weeping for the loss of her slipper,
and she had forgotten to tie up her long fair hair.

So the prince knew that he had found his bride, and that
she could cook and clean, and was not just an empty-headed

princess after all. She had found her prince, and he was handsome, young and rich enough to fulfill any dreams. Her father came to the wedding, and boasted that he had known it would be this way all the time.

And the old man? Well he married the hen-wife's daughter. He could save all his gold then, because he never had to buy fancy clothes for her, and neither did he mind that she was ugly as a troll, for his eyesight was none too good either.

Jock And His Mother

There was a poor widow woman once, who had only the one son. But one was enough.

Jock was a big daft lad who spent all morning lying in bed and all afternoon hanging about street corners, talking to his mates and combing his green spiky hair, while his mum – poor soul – worked very hard as a cleaner to keep them both.

"He's an idle big lump," the woman next door used to say. "I dinna ken why ye keep him like that. I'd turn him oot on his bike and mak' him look for a job."

"Ach, he's only a boy — and besides he needs his rest," said Jock's mum, and she worked harder than ever to earn enough to feed and clothe them both.

But at last the day came when even she had had enough.

"See here, Jocky," she said one morning, "this will not do. Ye'll need tae get oot o' that bed and find yirself a job tae try an' mak' a wee bit money."

"Aye, O.K. Ma," sighed Jock, rather unwillingly. "I'll see whit I can dae." He put on his best red tartan trousers and black leather jacket, gave his spikes an extra brush, pulled on the woolly hat with the pop group badges and set off to look for work.

The first person he met was a pedlar, travelling around the town selling ribbons and laces, tee-shirts and trousers, needles and pins from a huge suitcase.

"You carry my suitcase for me," said the pedlar, "And I'll give you a little something for yourself at night." So Jock lugged the heavy case in and out of houses, up and down tower blocks of flats. But most people shut the door very firmly when they saw him standing on the mat, so the pedlar did not make much money that day.

"I'm afraid I can only give you a very little something," he said, and opening his suitcase, he handed Jock the smallest thing he sold, which was a large darning needle.

Even Jock realised it was not going to make his mother all that happy, so on the way home he stopped to pick a bunch of wild flowers and put the needle in the middle of the bunch.

"Well," said his mother when she saw him. "And what hae ye done the day?" Jock told her about the pedlar and the needle.

"Aye, well, it's a start," said his mother. "And I could just be daen' wi' a big needle. Whit hae ye done wi'it?"

"It's in among the flooers, Ma!" said Jock, sticking the bedraggled bunch under her nose. "I brought them as a present for you."

"Very nice," sighed his mother. But although they searched through all the squashed and broken dandelions and daisies, the needle was nowhere to be found.

"You daft big lump!" she said. "Next time you're given something like that, stick it in your cap. That way ye winna loose it."

"Aw, right Ma," said Jock. "In my cap." She sighed and thumped his beefburger and chips on the table.

Next morning he set off to find work again. The day was bright and sunny, and rather than tramp the hot streets he thumbed a lift out into the country. It just happened that the man who gave him the lift was a traveller selling farm tools.

"If you give me a hand selling the stuff," said the traveller. "I'll give you something for yourself at the end of the day." So Jock spent the day going round farms with the traveller. He was the one who got out to open the gate if a dog was barking. He was the one who tramped across a dirty field of cows to find a farmer. And he was the one who hauled the bundles of tools in and out of the boot. But at the end of the day the traveller was quite pleased.

"Here you are," he said. "A wee something all to yourself." He reached into the back of the boot and took out a big old-fashioned scythe.

"Got it from someone in part-exchange for a lawnmower," he said. "It's all yours." Jock stood and watched the car vanishing down the road, and then looked at the big heavy scythe.

What was it his mother had said?

"Next time you're given something like that, stick it in your cap. That way ye winna loose it."

Jock looked at the rusty old scythe and then at his knitted cap with the pop badges pinned on it. Then he shrugged — and stuck the scythe through it.

It was a bit of a drag to wear, and the walk back to town was long and hot. Halfway he stopped by the river for a drink of cold water, but as he knelt down and leaned over to scoop up a mouthful, his cap, and the scythe fell in with a mighty splash.

"You daft great lummock!" howled his mother, when he told her the story. "You've lost the scythe and your cap as well. Whit wey did you no' tie it on a string and pull it behind you."

"Tie it on a string, and pull it . . ." said Jock. "I didna' think o' that. But I'll dae that next time, Ma. Don't you worry." She sighed, shook her head, and thumped his beefburger and chips on the table.

The following morning he set off, without his cap, to look for work again. He had had quite enough of travelling around so he went down to the local shops. The butcher was quite pleased to see him.

"You come to the meatmarket and help me load the van," he said. "And I'll see you get a rare leg of lamb for your dinner."

It would make a nice change from beefburgers thought Jock, so he spent the day working with the butcher, heaving around sides of sheep and cow, and sweeping out the shop. And sure enough, at closing time, the butcher thanked him and handed over a big juicy leg of lamb. Jock thanked him and stood on the pavement outside the shop staring at the meat.

What was it his mother had said?

"Whit wey did you no' tie it on a string and pull it behind you?"

So Jock hunted through his pockets for an old piece of string, tied it round the leg of lamb, and dragged it down the street home.

His mother heard him coming from a long way off. She stood at the door, with her arms folded and watched him. He was trailing something on the end of a string, and every dog in the district was fighting and snarling and clawing to get at whatever it was. By the time he arrived on the doorstep she saw that it was the remains of a leg of lamb, chewed, clawed and filthy.

"Whit's the matter, Ma?" said Jock seeing her speechless and purple with rage. "Ye tellt me tae tie it on a string."

"Next – time – ye great – daft – loon," she said beating out the words on his head with the bone. "Cairry it – ower – yir shoulder!"

"I'll mind that, Ma! I'll mind that!" said Jock trying to duck under the table.

Next morning he was up early, and off out before his mother.

It was Wednesday, market day in the town, so he headed down there to see if any of the farmers needed a hand. He met up with a pair of men who were selling horses.

"Yea, sure we could do with some help," said the little man with the thin moustache and the checked cap. "Couldn't we, Sid?"

"Yea, well," said Sid, peering at Jock through his dark glasses. "S'pose so, you're the Boss."

They parked their truck in a quiet back street and asked Jock to stand at the corner and watch out.

"For what?" said Jock. "Will I get something?"

"Just watch out!" snarled Sid. "Or you'll get something."

He opened the back of the truck and led out three horses and a small fat, wheezy pony.

Jock leaned against the corner, he was good at that, and watched. He watched people come and hand over money to the little man with the moustache, and go off with a horse, he watched as a big white car with a red stripe on the side drove up, and he watched as Sid and the Boss drove off in a hurry, leaving him with the little fat wheezy pony.

"That must be what they were going to give me," he decided, watching them vanish off down the road. He stood and stared at the pony, scratching his head.

What was it his mother had said?

"Next time," and she had really insisted on it, "cairry it ower yir shoulder!"

Jock took a deep breath and, much to the amazement of everybody watching, hefted the wee pony up over his shoulder. Then kicking, struggling, and falling over it, he set out for home.

He was just passing the big farmhouse that belonged to Sir Cuthbert and Lady Agatha McDosh when it happened that their daughter Deirdre was sitting in the sun lounge. Deirdre was a very pretty young lady, a big girl with a loud and jolly laugh, who had been very popular at school. But she was quickly becoming a great deal less popular, because since leaving school, she sat around all day with a face as long as a piece of string, and there was never a laugh to be had out of her.

"And don't waste time trying to make me laugh," she would sigh. "It's so b-o-o-oring!" She sat, day after day, looking like a wet Sunday, until her father, seeing all the young men losing interest, began to despair of ever having her happily married. He tried everything to make her laugh, but it was no use, and as a last resort he even offered to

marry her off, with a rich dowry to the first man who could make her laugh.

So there they were, Deirdre moping about in the sun lounge, and Sir Cuthbert and Lady Agatha taking tea by the parlour fire when a strange noise rang round the house.

"Mai goodness," Sir Cuthbert leapt to his feet. "Is thet laughter I hear?"

"It must be Deirdre!" said Lady Agatha, quite amazed, and sure enough, when they went to investigate, there was Deirdre, quite hysterical. She was rolling about the floor, holding her sides, and banging her heels, with the tears running down her cheeks.

"Most unladylike, dear!" gasped Lady Agatha. And then she glanced out of the window.

Poor Jock was struggling along the road, trying to carry the fat and wheezy little pony back home. The pony kicked and struggled, whinnied and wriggled. Jock yelled and fell over, his long thin legs tangled in the reins, with the pony rolling on top of him. Sir Cuthbert looked at his daughter rolling about the floor, and his wife giggling helplessly.

"Fetch that lad in here!" he roared. "We seem to have found a husband for our Deirdre."

So Deirdre and Jock were married, it was a very posh wedding with the bride all draped in lace and ribbons like a four-poster bed, and Jock in a red tartan kilt. He was tidied up, and the green spiked hair brushed flat for the occasion, but all the same every time Deirdre looked at him she could not help remembering the wee fat pony and snorted with laughter, until her father began to wish perhaps that she had stayed as she was.

The wedding party went on for three days and nights, and the guests were fed on the finest of food from Sir Cuthbert's farm. The choicest of that fine food was Lady Agatha's honey, which regularly won prizes at the local Farm Shows.

In the middle of the third night, Jock awoke, and fancying a sandwich and a glass of milk, shook Deirdre and asked where her mother kept the honey.

"It's in the round stone jar in the big cupboard in the kitchen," she said, and went back to sleep, still giggling.

Jock tiptoed downstairs and found the cupboard. Feeling around in the dark, his hands came on the wee round jar. He took the top off and stuck his finger in to lick out some honey, but the pot was almost empty, and he found he had to shove his whole hand right down inside.

Easy enough going in, but when he tried to pull his hand back out, he suddenly found it was stuck. He tugged and pulled, and heaved. The honey pot was firmly jammed on. He tiptoed round the kitchen in the dark, swinging out wildly, trying to break the pot on the side of the fireplace, but he missed and brought it down smartly on the head of one of the servants who had come down to see what the commotion was about.

"Help! Murder!" yelled the servant, rushing back out into the hall. He banged the gong at the bottom of the stairs to wake the rest of the household.

Jock, thoroughly frightened by the row, fled out of the back door into the darkness, and hid among the beehives, intending to stay there until the fuss had died down. He waited, and waited, as lights went off and on all over the house. At last, tired out, he fell asleep.

It was as he lay sleeping that Sid and the Boss came by. They had heard about the famous honey, and hatched a plot to steal the hives. They parked the truck at the end of the road, and tiptoed down the dark path lifting the hives and stuffing them into huge sacks.

"Here, they're gey heavy these," puffed Sid.

"Button it!" hissed the Boss. "Jist get on wi'it."

In the darkness they bundled up Jock and the hives together, then crept off, back towards the van, dragging the heavy sack between them.

As they came to the river Sid let his end of the sack thump to the ground, and sat down for a breather.

"Here, Boss!" he shouted, peering into the water. "You'll never believe this, but I've just found a cap, with a whacking great scythe stuck in it."

From the darkness of the night came a voice.

"Pit that doon, it's MY cap you've got there!"

"O-o-o-o-h, Mammy, it's haunted!" screamed Sid. "I'm gettin' oot o' this!"

He scrambled for the van closely followed by the Boss, leaving Jock to climb out of the sack, brush down his sticky pyjamas, and take the hives back to the house, where he was welcomed as a real hero by Lady Agatha, Sir Cuthbert and Deirdre.

"So you see," said his mother to the neighbours, as she went off to the supermarket in the mink coat he bought for her birthday. "I tellt ye all he was no sae daft."

And as for Jock, well, married to Deirdre, he lived happily ever after. He had so much money he could afford to stay in bed all morning, spend the afternoons hanging about street corners chatting to his mates, and have his hair spiked green, orange or even tartan if he fancied it.

Bibliography

Douglas, Sir George (selector and editor), *Scottish Fairy and Folk Tales*. Walter Scott, London, 1896

Galloway, Philippa. *Folk Tales from Scotland*. William Collins, London and Glasgow, 1943

Grierson, Elizabeth W. *Scottish Fairy Tales* T. Fisher Unwin, London 1910

Leodhas, Sorche Nic. *Thistle and Thyme – Tales and Legends from Scotland*. The Bodley Head, London 1965

Lyford-Pike, Margaret. *Scottish Fairy Tales*. J. M. Dent, London 1974

Popular Rhymes of Scotland. William and R. Chambers, Edinburgh and London, 1841